NOT SICK ENOUGH
TO DIE...

My Leap
from Patient to Naturopathic Doctor

SHERIN LEE ND CNC
Foreword by David Knezetich

Library of Congress Control Number: 2016954140
ISBN-13:   Paperback: 978-1-63524-410-6
             PDF: 978-1-63524-411-3
             ePub: 978-1-63524-412-0
             Kindle: 978-1-63524-413-7

Printed in the United States of America

LitFire LLC
1-800-511-9787
www.litfirepublishing.com
order@litfirepublishing.com

CONTENTS

I am not a medical doctor, and I am in no way giving medical advice.

I am a certified Naturopath and Nutritionist ND, CNC. All information is expressly the opinion and belief of the author.

Only as far as I can reach...
can I grasp

Only as clearly as I envision...
can I see

Only as deeply as I believe...
can I receive

ACKNOWLEDGEMENTS

Dr. Tei-Fu Chen and **Dr. Oi-Lin Chen**, whose herbal knowledge and expertise have presented my life with health opportunities I never dreamt possible.

David Knezetich, loyal friend and longtime client, without whose editorial abilities and prodding this book would not have met its publisher.

Veronica Rodriguez, my trusted loyal friend and right hand.

Andrew Womack. A resource of unquestionable knowledge, who continues to teach me "the Gospel Truth". And who has the true "Gift of Teaching".

W. Clement Stone. My one-time employer, mentor, and author. W. Clement taught me self-discipline, self-worth, and integrity. He instructed me on the need to constantly control my emotions which would ordain my destiny and aid me in challenging times.

Joel Osteen. A wonderful, charismatic "Man of God", who understands the challenges for people in the world today. He can take the darkest of times and bring in the sunshine. His ability to raise anyone's hope is truly God-given.

Robert H. Schuler, who guided me through multiple deaths of immediate family members. He opened my mind and my heart with his autobiography "Prayer: My Soul's Adventure with God". I recall hobbling up to him on my crutches for his autograph. After signing his name, he looked up at me and continued to write: "YOU are an answer to prayer! Just LOOK in the mirror." What an inspiration and what a prediction.

Loyal Clients and True Friends:

> *Tony and Carol Doszak*
> *Jo Anne and Doc Furbee*
> *Barbara Burk*
> *Tallat Choudry*
> *Gayle Lakie*

FOREWORD BY THE EDITOR

Greetings, Gentle Reader. I'm in the unusual position of being both literary assistant and editor to Sherin Lee in the creation of this book, and the writer of its foreword.

Her book details her struggles to overcome multiple health challenges, leading her to pursue a career as a Doctor of Naturopathy and ultimately to write this book for the purpose of both informing and helping others with their health challenges. The primary reason I was asked by Sherin to work with her on this project is that she felt I had a fairly good understanding of the "big picture" of how things worked as she helped her clients achieve better health. In addition, having known each other all our lives I knew about her background, and I am also her client. Make no mistake about it: Sherin, a Board Certified Naturopath and Nutritionist, is the "real deal". She has had to meet her own health challenges. In a prior career, Sherin was a hard-driving, record-setting, award-winning salesperson of insurance. Unfortunately from a health standpoint, in her day-to-day activities she was burning the candle at both ends: Not enough sleep, chain smoking, bad food. Healthwise, she was a train wreck waiting to happen.

Not quite. That "train wreck" turned out to be a car wreck. The results of the accident included broken bones, brain damage, chronic fatigue, fibromyalgia, and reliving the trauma of the event through frequent nightmares. After multiple testings, she was found to have an 8th-grade IQ. Without dispute, this qualified her for permanent disability assistance for several years. Most importantly, she was diagnosed and treated for clinical depression, and at that point became suicidal.

After thus hitting rock bottom, she knew it was time to find a way to get better. The fact that she has recovered so well physically and the strides she has made academically after this accident are, to my mind, remarkable.

As for myself as her client, a few years ago my diet, weight, and body shape made it abundantly clear that I was not far off from a stroke or similar disaster. Quite simply, I might not be around today to write these words, or I might be merely existing in a nursing home.

Working together on my condition, this health bullet was dodged. A few years later, in middle age I found myself suffering from shingles. I learned that shingles can be a long-term affliction and can reoccur. Working with Sherin Lee again, my shingles disappeared in a few weeks and as of this writing have not reoccurred in several years.

As Sherin explained to me, a major principle of Naturopathy is that when given the proper nutrition along with the removal of harmful substances, the body will heal itself. In Sherin's words, Naturopathy shows us how to get out of the body's way in order to let the body perform its own miracle.

In writing this book, we have sought a writing style that is plain, unembellished and direct, much as how friends or relatives would speak to each other when sharing information around the kitchen table. "Make it clear and simple, and therefore understandable" became our guiding principle. Our goal was to banish medical jargon, so that we can be confident that you, the reader, will have your needs met.

David Knezetich

INTRODUCTION BY THE AUTHOR

It was years after my recovery and I had never stopped to consider that I had a story which could affect the lives of many in their attitudes, beliefs, and even their actions. With this passing of time also came more and more despair disguised as normalcy within the people coming through my office. Through personal experience I learned that despair was not normal for anyone. Yet some people appeared resigned to the acceptance that this could be their fate; without the realization that no matter how difficult life becomes, better health could bring more optimism. Having told my story many, many times, I had arrived at the point to where it had begun to bore me. Making comparisons of health issues with others had become monotonous to me.

To that day no one had ever matched me in the severity of physical and mental injuries, and above all, hopelessness... until one day....And on this day I was meeting with a big, burly, solemn-looking gentleman. He informed me that he had never received any form of encouragement through the years in which he had sought medical treatment for various ailments. And he actually stated he had been discouraged by many health professionals advising him that his life would never return to normal. Once again I would pull my story from my memory bank and present it to him in a most heartfelt manner. He had been looking down, and as I ended the story he lifted his head and looking me directly in the eye — he began to cry as though his heart would break — he caught his breath and whispered, "I can be well". And I could not hold back my tears.

This is the moment in which this book was conceived. It was astonishing to see such results. If this man's heart could be touched so deeply and from it spring such hope — without any evidence — how many others could be touched and moved to the belief that anything is possible, if only you believe.

I also believe that much of my writing is for the purpose of my own redemption.

Many of us live through short seasons of favor and some never experience favorable seasons at all. You might say that many times we get what we have expected. I have longed for an opportunity to share my life with you in the hope it will bring to you "an attitude of expectancy". Because in my experience I have found it necessary to warm the heart in order to thaw the numbness that has formed.

We can be victims or victors. We can live in the darkness or live in the light. Either way we were born with the right to choose. Myself, I love my life with all its colorful twists and turns. Grateful to awaken to each new day with an opportunity to change the lives of those I am fortunate enough to touch.

My life has been blessed and favored by writing this book — your life will be blessed and favored in reading this book.

1

FALLING FROM LIFE

The journey begins on a sunny morning in mid-May. Birds were singing; the sun was shining its brightest, reflecting my feeling that life had never been sweeter. I was prospering, and my position as an insurance agent had driven me to become one of the top one-half of one percent in the nation. I was believing at that moment that I was invincible, and in the very next instant the inconceivable happened. Little did I know that when I approached the traffic light in order to gain access to the expressway, this would be the last moment of happiness known to me for a very long time to come. Without the slightest warning the serenity of the moment was broken by squealing tires, shattering glass, and a powerful crash.

Then there was silence...and then the familiar sound of an ambulance siren off in the distance, filling the quiet.

Subjectively, everything happened in a flash. One moment the sun was shining...the next moment someone had turned off the lights....I was in total darkness.

As I awoke on the passenger seat from this unconscious state, I found myself in an incoherent haze. The first thing of which I became aware was my head being held by another and being assured that "everything was fine". At that point I opened my eyes and looked down.

The lovely, soft pink blouse I was wearing was now totally scarlet red against my black suit. Blood was pouring profusely down my face and into my eyes from a hole in my head, a broken nose, and facial cuts.

Another bit of knowledge was to be revealed later to me: Little did I know that these waking moments after this horrible crash would in reality be the beginning moments of the ending of life as I had known it.

The stranger holding my hand was a true blessing. The situation could have been dramatically more severe due to the degree of blood loss, had he not set me upright and acted to slow the bleeding. It was explained to me that upon impact with the door handle on the passenger's side of the car, the skull had stopped, but the brain had continued to spin. The bone in the front of the skull **cut** the connection between the right and left lobes. *Past and present memory were gone!*

There was an overwhelming feeling of hopelessness as the paramedics gently and efficiently lifted my limp body with its various broken bones into the waiting ambulance. Though I was in a mental daze at that time, I can recall their voices conveying a sense of urgency as they spoke among themselves. They radioed ahead in preparation for my future treatment at the hospital's emergency center. It felt as if I were dreaming, and even though I could not understand what was being said, it felt as if I were eavesdropping on someone else's life-or-death medical condition.

With regard to my initial thoughts and observations upon waking in the emergency room, there were none — I honestly have no recollection. The earliest memory I do recall is that of my oldest brother standing over me as I lay on a table, shaking his head, with tears running down his cheeks. I remember this because his tears had wet my face. This was my first clue that there was more damage to my body this time than in previous accidents. Ironically, this accident had resulted in a second head injury involving the *opposite* side of the brain.

As mentioned earlier, my husband and I were employed as insurance agents, and traveling was a normal part of our lives. That day, he was out of town and it took some time to reach him. I felt a sense of relief when he finally got to the hospital. That *familiarity*, that sense of *being at home*, of *being comfortable*, can give you a false sense of security. At that time his presence comforted me to the point that I felt certain my recovery would be swift and complete — as it had been many times in the past.

* * * *

Throughout the initial period of my hospitalization my family members showed no real concern for my condition, nor did the doctors attending my case. Because of my tenacious nature, they may have looked upon this "incident" as just another injury in a series of injuries throughout my accident-prone life: another health crisis added to the challenges I had weathered in the past, such as leukemia, bouts of walking pneumonia, and last but certainly not least, bouts with cancer.

It actually would take some time before I fully realized that every aspect of my life would be negatively impacted by the present situation. The rapidity of my decline would eventually and totally consume my life like a fire burning out of control, and nothing or no one would be capable of stopping its progression.

After some minor testing—and of course resting—I had appeared sufficiently healed. Excited to return to work and being committed to completing a previous project, I cared less about how I was feeling. Determination, driven by pride, pushed me to prove my resiliency. After all, I had ignored pain and discomfort many times in the past. The good news was that I was always successful; the bad news was that this time I was failing miserably and falling into rapid decline.

Serious symptoms began to surface. At the top of the list were migraine headaches and blurred vision. Out of nowhere came a speech impediment—I began to stutter. Also developing was a lack of observation and concentration, which would cause me to become lost in familiar places. Simple instructions became impossible to understand, or if understood, to follow. I began to miss traffic stop signs and had been stopped by authorities for driving through traffic lights. These phenomena were only a few of the suspicious changes I began to notice. And I was not the only one to notice them. As my personality began to change, my managers became concerned and suggested I return to the hospital for observation and evaluation once again.

In my going through a second diagnosis, the doctors learned that they had actually misdiagnosed my condition the first time. After some of the most sophisticated tests, it was determined that I had in reality suffered severe brain damage due to oxygen deprivation and was suffering from PTSD (Post-Traumatic Stress

Disorder). There was no way to "sugar-coat" such a blatant misdiagnosis!

This would prove to be a rude awakening for us all. At this time it was determined that my intelligence had been reduced to a 2nd-grade equivalency. Upon hearing this prognosis, it was as though the very breath had been knocked from my lungs.

Now I was going to rehabilitation at the hospital on a full-time basis. My initial contact was with the head of the Rehabilitation Center. I was told by this person that it was unfortunate that I had not been brought to them when the injury originally occurred. She told me that because of the passing of time, my brain patterns had become set and it would become very difficult if not impossible to change them. With a prognosis such as this, a less determined person would have turned around and gone back home, never to return — *but not me.*

My day at the center began with the use of flash cards to relearn addition and subtraction, just simple math. To test my recall I scanned mindlessly through articles and texts, which in reality meant nothing to me and were quickly forgotten, but which a grade-school student would have absorbed with ease. The use of the "Five W's" — *Who, What, When, Where, and Why* — was totally useless to me in my condition. The God-given gift of comprehension was no longer available to me.

Along with the stutter mentioned previously came a serious balance problem. Coming on suddenly, without warning, I would simply fall to the floor. I recall an incident which happened with my husband which was extremely embarrassing to both of us. I had taken a ride with him on a prospective sales call. While walking up to the front door, without notice I fell to the ground.

Seeing the look on his face was almost unbearable for me to behold; I imagined he would never again ask me to accompany him on business.

As this problem with balance persisted, I was not encouraged by the many suggestions given by the Rehabilitation Center. One suggestion was to sit myself on a giant ball, which I was to then "walk" around the room with the aid of my already non-existent sense of balance. Obviously, I fell from the ball much more often than I ever walked it! Much later, I corrected this balance problem for myself. Body weaknesses must be strengthened *from within.* The ball exercise would never prove successful until the gland in the brain which controls balance was strengthened.

The migraine headaches were the worst kind of torture. Overall, I experienced these for multiple years: They caused tormenting, agonizing shooting pains throughout my head.

Any type of light was terribly painful, and the simple act of walking across the room was unbearable to every fiber of my body! There was a feeling of vibration, difficult to explain, which accompanied a feeling of electrical responses like shocks throughout my body.

At this time the company that employed me was expressing concern that I was not improving. They wished to hasten my return to active employment, and they sent their best and brightest medical staff to speak to the head of the hospital's Rehabilitation Department. The representatives of the insurance company proposed my transfer to a rehabilitation clinic in the suburbs of Chicago which catered to young professionals and executives with similar issues. In the previous correspondence sent to my employer, the Rehabilitation Center continuously alluded to my "complexity", blaming it for my lack of improvement. But in spite of my complexity, the Rehabilitation Center would not sign off on my transfer. They reasoned that I was in such a horrendous condition due to my physical disabilities and my depressed mental state that a change of environment could bring about another, more serious breakdown. Conclusively, the doctor refused to take responsibility should they sign off on my case and something more radical were to happen. I was very resentful of this situation. It took a very long period of time for me to forgive the people who in effect kept me captive and held me back.

Continuing to remain at the center, my treatment was multi-faceted. It extended to routine psychiatric treatment, including some of the best drugs man had been able to produce in order to "Trick AND Treat" the mind.

I was presented with four different opinions from various psychiatrists and psychologists. Probably the strangest suggestion was that I begin holding "White Glove Parties", such as had been originated by Jackie Kennedy Onassis. That suggestion certainly called into question which one of us needed treatment, or at the very least a reality check!

This brings up questions I've always thought about: With all the time I'd spent in the company of doctors, not even one ever asked me what I was eating, or if I considered a possible link between smoking and migraine headaches.

This was especially so of the neuropsychologist I spent time with, eating and smoking on a regular basis.

Time passed and I became even more despondent, especially after being informed that I would never be capable of being employed again due to the inability to comprehend or learn. I was to be placed in a government program of permanent disability and was to continue the weekly psychiatric visits from my favorite neuropsychologist, Dr. James Quinlan.

With the above-mentioned conditions, along with the previous diagnoses of chronic fatigue and fibromyalgia, my depression was all-consuming. In addition, no one had even remotely affected the severity of my migraine headaches. I slept a tremendous number of hours, and in an effort to stay awake a few hours each day I smoked cigarettes, drank gallons of coffee, consumed candies called "Skittles", and drank cans of "Juicy Juice", to be specific.

This was the diet I lived on in order to stay awake for a few hours when my husband arrived home for the weekend after being on the road all week. I am sure he could have chosen to return home each day, but I am also sure he wondered to whom and what he would be arriving home to....So it was much less stressful for him to stay away with the exception of weekends. Consequently, on weekdays I spent very little time doing anything other than sleeping. Since light entering from outdoors could cause a painful headache, the window shades were always kept closed. My home had become almost like an aboveground tomb. With being alone all the time, I became a true recluse. I believe that because I was not falling down or bleeding profusely, no one around me seemed capable or willing to acknowledge the degree of serious damage I had incurred. During this time I eventually developed an ever-deepening hole I called *lonesomeness*. I felt I had become burdensome to those around me, resulting in my becoming more withdrawn. And this is about the time I began to want out of my life.

* * * *

Next came another hurdle, this one concerning my driving abilities. I had not been driving an automobile simply because I was never leaving the safety of my home. However, now I was told to go to a suburban hospital which had the resources to actually observe and determine if I should be allowed to drive an automobile. The model of vehicle used for the driving road test was equipped with a steering wheel, a gas pedal, and a brake pedal on both driver and passenger sides.

I was accompanied by an observer and my husband. If you had been with us, you would have been terrified. I was not warned in advance that I would be tested on an expressway. As I approached the entrance ramp of the expressway, I became so overwhelmed and confused by the whizzing traffic that I simply stomped on the accelerator petal and the vehicle lurched out into the traffic as I began to weave from lane to lane. My husband, who was in the back seat, just about became permanently molded into its upholstery!

It was decided at that point that my driving would be limited to a radius of two blocks around my home.

I had gone from a life of total fearlessness to one of fearfulness. Coming from an optimist, full of dreams, to being an isolated, depressed prisoner existing within my home.

I thought I had been holding myself together, but now I was quickly falling into a well of hopelessness from which I truly felt there would be no return.

* * * *

I was still seeing psychiatrists and psychologists at the time, and had just about run through the entire range of antidepressants, pain and sleep medications. Sitting impatiently in the doctor's office one day, waiting for an already-tardy psychiatrist to arrive for my appointment, I struck up a conversation with a girl whose actions were rather peculiar.

She casually mentioned how she had just arrived back from a trip to the hospital, after an attempt to take her own life.

Becoming curious, I perked up, as I had not been interested in anything in a very long time but had also entertained thoughts on the same subject. Her attempt on her life was to be accomplished, she explained, by saving up multiple pills, and then taking them all at one time. This seemed simple enough to me. As noted earlier, the connection between the right and left lobes of my brain had been severed by the accident. As a result, my memory was pretty much "missing in action". But this girl, having both pencil and paper, acted as my instructor. She began to write a Prescription for Suicide. This one, she assured me, was foolproof....How ironic that she lived to tell that it was "foolproof"!

When I finally entered the doctor's office and took a seat, the first thing he asked me straight out was if I planned on using the newly-discovered information from my co-conspirator. Whoa! Was the waiting room "bugged", had the girl and I simply been overheard, or had he seen the word *suicidal* written on my forehead? I do not believe I ever answered his question. The fact that another person should have overheard my intention was both humiliating and embarrassing. I realized what action he would take.

He would begin withholding the drugs I had been taking; although unbeknownst to him, I had a warehouse full of unopened drugs at my home.

He put me on what he termed a "suicide watch". To this day I still have not concluded what the term meant. Though my appointments became much more frequent during this period, nevertheless no one was ever around to watch me. I realized later — it was GOD! Looking back now, it's obvious that there was plenty of alone time for me to have accomplished the deed. Rather than being an ironclad prevention against my committing suicide, the suicide watch simply generated more income for my psychiatrist because of the additional appointments during this period. The drugs made me neurotic — I was already neurotic enough and did *not* need any enhancement!

"Neurotic" has been defined as disturbed, unstable, high-strung, troubled, paranoid, and a victim of depression. Ironic, isn't it. The anti-depressant drugs made me feel more depressed!

* * * *

We can never realize the value and significance of emotional stability until it is no longer in our possession. I often looked in the mirror during this period and did not recognize the image of the person shown there. My eyes were bloodshot, lacking moisture and luster, with a painful appearance.

The eye is the lamp of the body. So if your eye is sound, your entire body will be full of light.
— Matthew 6:22

* * * *

There was no doubt about it. My downward spiral over this long period of time had been exacerbated, if not caused, by the misdiagnosis of my original medical condition. This delay in diagnosis had lead to an even greater progression of the traumatic damage experienced internally by my body.

Henry David Thoreau once said that "Most men lead lives of quiet desperation". He was so right, although in my case life was quite desperate but certainly not quiet. It was like a clanging bell, coming from the constant pain in my head, the ringing in my ears, and the aches throughout the various broken and dislocated bones of my body.

* * * *

One constantly makes decisions, large and small, in the process of daily living; although, when you no longer have control over your own mind, these choices are no longer yours to make. *Decisions determine destiny.* In which case I had neither a determination nor a destiny.

Unfortunately, mental illnesses, brain damage, and Post-Traumatic Stress Disorder (PTSD) are not always visible and conclusively identifiable by those around us. People could not be blamed for their lack of sympathy when I myself, the sufferer, was unable to understand the situation and no one in the medical establishment was offering any legitimate explanation.

This calls to mind the fact that a person who does not understand you can be mentally crippling to yourself as well. An example of this was the situation with my former husband exhorting me to get back up and resume my life as if nothing had happened: He did not understand that just because at that point I was not on crutches or wheelchair bound, my lack of mental faculties had rendered me even *more* crippled than either of the other two scenarios. But the pressure can be very harmful to the recovery process.

In a conversation I had with Bill (my former husband) in the course of writing this book, he stated that for him the most horrific part of this situation was the *not knowing* if he would find me still alive when he came home.

His feeling about my condition was that the years of depression were extremely difficult, but when I went into years of apathy, that was even *more* unbearable.

Overall, the steps taken for my recovery had had no effect; each day I was steadily being torn down. Years of violent waking from nightmares as I hurled myself from the bed, tangled in bed sheets and blankets, was taking its toll on my back and neck and to a lesser extent my head. During all this time, I never really ate anything of nutritional value. As mentioned previously, I lived on stimulants in order to stay awake for a few hours, particularly when my husband was home on the weekends. Coordinating a meal was very difficult.

Watching one food item cook was mentally exhausting; serving a meal with three food items was excruciating.

Operating a food processor was too complicated. I recall an incident that amazes me even after all this time. A few years ago I purchased a simple food processor having only three interchangeable blade attachments. Embarrassingly, I gave this brand-new machine to my cousin because I was unable to master it, as its "learning curve" was too complicated for me! Sometime later I asked for it back (after my cousin mentioned he did not use it), and now it was simple to operate. Wow! Amazing! We were never told that we could become more intelligent, more able to learn as we got older; instead, we are told the opposite. We expect that there comes an age when life stops giving us things, and instead begins taking them away — things such as health, memory, strength. This is NOT my belief, and it never was. However, we cannot use wishful thinking to achieve this goal — we must have a plan.

We must become "greedy" in our aging. We must trust and believe that anything we desire is not only *obtainable* but *retainable,* until such time as we desire otherwise. No matter where your physical and mental health registers on your personal scale, improvement can be just ahead if you're looking for it.

Note: The passing of time cannot kill you. The only thing that *can* kill you...disease or accident.

But I could not let these challenges be known to my husband or others — it was too humiliating! The person who was once the high-powered, successful, results-driven sales professional could now barely put two thoughts together!

The scars on my arm are a permanent reminder of where I came from. Certain pain receptors were not functioning correctly, and neither was my physical coordination. I was burned while cooking with the broiler oven: I was totally unaware of what was happening until I smelled the burning flesh and noticed my skin turn white. The consequence of this was that I simply could not cook when I was alone.

Another painful lesson to be learned.

2

"WE WILL KEEP AN EYE ON IT"

Early Days I

L ooking back, it is clear that the origins of my post-accident challenges did not lie entirely in that catastrophe.

Conditions and environmental factors in my early adolescence certainly fertilized the ground, if not predisposed me for the situation in which I found myself after the accident. The accident itself was merely the catalyst for the changes yet to come in my life.

It seems to me that from the beginning, the deck was heavily stacked against the prospect of my having a healthy life.

Born the third of four children, the others being boys, I grew up more tomboy than girl. Only much later as an adult did I realize that a good portion of my life had been lived with a hormonal imbalance. I was often accused of being insensitive and unfeeling, with an adrenaline-fueled competitive drive, unlike others of my gender.

These severe imbalances made me oblivious or indifferent to many of the physical problems that were manifesting as my body was growing and developing. Plagued with a weak immune system, my body was under continuous attack from a variety of sicknesses and diseases.

Western medicine looks upon various issues as being normal in childhood. Realistically, if a child's immune system is strong, he or she will not encounter these so-called "childhood diseases".

Continuous weaknesses persistently kept me from attending primary school on a regular basis. In addition to a poor attendance record came even poorer grades and an inability to pay attention, and to actually learn anything being taught. Adding fuel to this already-existing fire was the fact that there were *weeks* at a time when I would not have a bowel elimination! I recall being taken many times to a medical doctor (M.D.) and my mother being told by him that "some people just do not eliminate every day and some do not eliminate for numerous days". Little did neither I nor anyone around me realize that my poor little body was poisoning itself — and it would continue to do so for several years to come.

Allow me to catalog some of the diseases of my childhood: During the winter months I fought chronic bouts with influenza, colds and fevers, escalating to chronic tonsillitis and strep throats, along with eye, ear and sinus infections. I also experienced chronic constipation, migraine headaches, breathing problems with bronchitis, aches and pains in my stomach, muscle cramps, fragile bones, and tissues with a constant display of bruises. Not to mention suffering from psoriasis and allergies. As these periods of sickness seemed to last longer and longer, I was bombarded with stronger and stronger antibiotics and penicillin regimens. Suffering from fallen arches, I was required to wear ugly shoes especially designed for me.

By the time I reached the 8th grade of primary school, my roster of maladies had grown to include hair loss and poor vision, for which I wore bifocals with glass lenses the thickness of a soda bottle. Dental cavities which developed into periodontal gum disease requiring multiple surgeries. Upon the arrival of my menstrual cycle, the profuse bleeding and blood clotting I suffered resulted in my receiving treatment for anemia. My physical appearance at this time was thus: a pale face with thinning hair and eyebrows, a large bust and a flat *derrière*, and an extremely bloated stomach with a thick waist.

Learning became more and more of a challenge. Summer school had become a yearly requirement. At this time I would like to relate a personal observation regarding children with learning disabilities and behavioral disturbances. This predisposition to mental weaknesses does not just fall from the sky, spreading as if it were an epidemic. Just as in my case, it develops over time, from lifestyle habits lived with and including generational weaknesses. Had labels such as ADD (Attention Deficit Disorder) existed during my childhood I would have been thus stamped, classified, and pigeonholed, just as so many other children are stamped. This would have given me the perfect excuse to fail in life.

A lack of discipline and an equal lack of desire to learn made life extremely difficult for my parents. I was expelled multiple times from the private school and private academy I attended. Looking back, it saddens me as I am sure my actions brought them great embarrassment and frustration.

All of these unhappy circumstances certainly could have been avoided had my brain and body been properly nourished and the weaknesses of my body strengthened and made well. It was always a case of treating the symptom — never looking for an overall cause. Again, it is my belief that we can keep unfavorable, inherited weaknesses out of our lives if and when we become conscious of our everyday habits and the habits of our forefathers.

I wish to take a moment here and thank God for the incredibly strong body given me to withstand the onslaught of health issues that tore me down physically and mentally on a daily basis.

Early Days II

For the majority of my life I was unclear as to what I actually wanted for myself. At one point I even thought I wanted to be a Catholic nun. However, the good sisters convinced me that I would *not* do well, due to a discipline problem and a very large chip on my shoulder. So I tried *everything* except that.

After barely graduating high school, I moved to "The Windy City", Chicago, Illinois. My scholastic background had not prepared me for much. My typing was lackadaisical and my shorthand was almost illegible. In spite of these deficiencies, I got a job as a secretary. During the following years there were so many job changes in multiple occupations that I lost count of them all. Life to me at that time was lackluster and my interest was purely financial. How much money could I make and how much could I spend? So I worked two and sometimes three jobs at one time in my early adult years. Friends supplied me with Benzedrine and sleeping pills as a way to alternately get myself "up" for my day and to "come down" at the end of it. My diet became even more void of anything of value, as I was now living to a large degree on drugs, alcohol, and cigarettes.

On multiple occasions, my menstrual period caused me to hemorrhage. These occurrences were something I would just ride out. It never occurred to me to seek medical treatment. Good health or bad was never something of which I made an issue.

As time progressed, I became extremely thin and was advised by my employer at the time that I needed to seek medical advice. My appearance was just an outward sign that my physical foundation was beginning to visibly crack. Thyroid disease, exhaustion of the adrenal glands, endometriosis, irritable bowel syndrome, and extremely painful colitis would not have been apparent to others. I had been doing modeling as one of my manifold occupations. To me, my appearance was more valuable than my health. So I simply wore a variety of wigs to hide my problem with thinning hair.

I ignored the warning signs these conditions represented. Instead my solution was to take more drugs, never giving a second thought to changing my lifestyle. My attitude became ferocious at the suggestion of giving up any of my bad habits! Meals at this time consisted of red meat and potatoes in any form, in addition to heavily-salted, high-fat and high-sugar foods.

While living in the city, waiting outdoors for trains and buses during the winter months pushed my body into experiencing bouts of bronchitis and walking pneumonia. My lungs became so congested that some nights I would wake from sleep gasping for breath, feeling as though I were drowning.

Ironically, that is just what happens; you drown. My father passed away from pneumonia, drowning in his own mucus which filled his lungs until he could no longer draw a breath.

The primary thought I would like to leave with the reader after reviewing my catalog of medical issues is just this: Everything I have listed above could have been avoided...as I was forced to learn later.

Early Days III

Looking back at this point in my career, it is clear that I had ambition, drive, and motivation, but not the physical and mental capacity to utilize them for what I could have accomplished. My bad habits and addictions were so strong that I never ever speculated about changing my life, nor had I any desire to do so or the willpower to make it happen.

> **"Every saint has a past; every sinner has a future."**
> —**Oscar Wilde**

As time went on I knew I needed to learn to drive a car, much later than American adolescents usually learn to drive. It was a difficult challenge for me; but living in The Windy City, I had been able to put it off. I was learning that my response time and alertness were not very efficient, and it would become apparent to me later. However, it wasn't apparent to the person behind the wheel at that time, ME. My vision was poor, and even with glasses my night vision was very fuzzy and blurry. It's truly a wonder, what with the multiple accidents, traffic tickets, drivers license suspensions, etc., that I am still here to write about it. My biggest regret is that we can never go back and undo any harm done to another through our neglect!

In those years, I thought that anyone with vision problems would be experiencing the same lack of vision when driving at night as I did. Since then, I've learned about the connection between our vision and the liver. The liver is the "oil filter" of our bodies. When the liver is having difficulty cleansing the blood, *where are all those toxins?* That's right, they're still in the blood. *The dirtier the blood,* I've found, *the poorer the vision.*

My blood was obscenely contaminated from an early age. My vision was becoming poorer and poorer, especially at night.

Sometime later, my usual eye doctor referred me to an eye specialist. The result of this appointment was that I was diagnosed with the onset of glaucoma. It was interesting to me that I received the same standard response that I had received from the psychiatrist: "We will keep an eye on it." I've often wondered if the good doctor ever consciously considered the irony in that remark: He would keep his eyes on my eyes; and as I would be losing my vision, what benefit would I have reaped from my eyes being watched? Or was this simply a misunderstanding?

As I returned for my various doctor appointments, I was being "looked at" but nothing was being done to change the situation — and nothing *could* be done at that point in time.

3

A MESSAGE OF HOPE AND HEALING

I had made the decision to remove myself from rehabilitation because I had a new direction. The staff there had done all they could for me, and I will be eternally grateful to the professionals who once again taught me the basics of reading, writing, and arithmetic. However, overall I was not improving in other areas such as healing, living without constant pain, having a memory I could depend on, and in general moving forward with my life. It was time to move in another direction, and as I moved away from mainstream medicine, opposition began to develop. I allowed my family, friends, and even strangers to steal my peace of mind about my decision to seek alternatives in health care.

As I sought a solution in alternative medicine it was blatantly evident that everyone was not going to agree with a medical approach that was as *old* as man, while also being, to most, a concept as *new* as today's newborn...particularly with the acceptance of theories and techniques which were viewed by others as "out-of-the-normal". In order to cope with criticism and with becoming somewhat of an outcast for my choice of health care, I *forced* myself to ignore the whispers of others and not to feel rejected for my ideas and actions. Instead this brought about self-knowledge which would serve me well in the future.

As an individual, I would need to set my resolve that *no one* could ever interrupt the path I was now pursuing.

Self-examination gave me the knowledge of WHY I was being influenced by others — influenced even though I knew in my heart that my alternative path was right.

The "healing techniques" to be engaged in were being done at a time when the words "herbs" and "supplements" were never imagined, let alone being practiced in mainstream medicine without the word "caution" being attached.

Later I realized that it was my low self-esteem that allowed their opinions to matter so much to me. Did I not have a valuable opinion of myself and my intelligence? Did others really know better than I what was best for my life? Recognition that my personal happiness and acceptance of my life depended solely upon myself — never upon another. My life would be lived as it always had been, independently.

Beginning the pilgrimage to the promised land would not have a map nor would the destination be in view. Only a promise. Human history has proven that we all have something we ultimately believe in, even if it is only ourselves. For most of my life, it was "*I* could do all things," period.

When I found myself falling flat on my face, there came a dawning. The fact that *I* could no longer do it alone would be the overriding thought at those times when my damaged brain was capable of lucid thinking. What could I need? *I needed God....*

My recipe for recovery was to take one step and stay there for a lengthy period of time, getting myself into a habit through doing it again and again. This was necessary as I could not store or remember the sequence in which something had been done.

I began with judging the worth and importance of foods at the grocery store, specifically the fruits and vegetables in the fresh produce department. You cannot force your body to accept certain foods that it just does not enjoy. So it was slim pickings for me as I chose the very few raw vegetables which my body would be willing to accept or simply tolerate.

As mentioned previously, for some time my diet consisted of candies, cigarettes, and fruit juice, and I had no interest in "live" food. The fact is that I used outside stimulants to replace the lack of materials within the body which facilitate a true enjoyment of life. At this time I was living through years of chronic fatigue, when I had no energy and slept most of the day. This grocery store activity was the only successful means by which I could motivate myself into a few hours of awake time.

It always astonishes me that my heart or some other vital organ did not fail during this period. Would you believe it if I told you I never even gave a first thought to food or what I ate with regard to my handicapped existence? No one ever told me that the food I was eating — or not eating! — was creating even bigger, deeper obstacles to my dream of becoming physically whole again. Allow me to revise that last statement. Never in my life had I been whole, though to those around me I gave a great performance of being healthy and happy. I had always been sickly in some capacity and now I was speculating on having total freedom from weaknesses in the future.

On further examination it could be said that I was **living to die** just as, sadly enough, many are **dying to live**. I relished my life-stealing habits, even *after* my accident, and for a time was unwilling to surrender these habits. I believed they were bringing me pleasure. Always being on guard, always being protective of that which I felt I had the right to hold on to. How unsound of mind is that thinking?

This is the attitude which would hasten my demise — and frankly lead to my sickly, diseased, early death.

After thinking back on my evasion of death from cancer of the female organs or from leukemia, I was finally recognizing my insanity. The light of dawn was finally arriving. Oftentimes, I speak or write of getting a picture. In this instance, when my epiphany came, so did a visual picture in all its clarity and detail. I saw an old woman with a wrinkled face who was going bald, dragging her right leg, with multiple aches and pains from two "whiplash" injuries and the pains of eight different broken bones. A woman suffering from sclerosis and osteoporosis and assaults up and down the spine, whose mind had become so lost it was not to be found again — *that* is what I saw. Now, how is *that* for a picture to inspire you?

* * * *

Belief in a dream is a wish your heart makes and when the desire is in your heart, *your dream will manifest in its physical form.* I did not have a plan, but I did have an approach. The germ of this was a phrase I had heard as a Bible interpretation:

"Life gives Life". At the time I had no idea what that phrase really meant. However, I came to realize and believe that if I continued to eat dead, I would stay dead; and ultimately this became the bedrock of my approach.

From now on I would be entering a period which would include the prevention of further injury and a path of healthy treatment on an ongoing basis. I was beginning to desire a better quality of health, one to which no relative of mine had ever given a thought. The unhealthiness of my relatives encompassed cancer to Parkinson's and everything in between. I was determined to find the causes of the pain riddling my body. Among other weaknesses, I would find a way to strengthen my motor skills. The desire to eliminate stuttering-stammering speech and bodily weakness, along with my premature aging and the loss of the many physical attributes I once enjoyed and admired in myself, was becoming more intense by the day.

There would be no more hiding of my physical wounds, nor concealment of my mental and emotional dependencies by hiding myself away. I would no longer allow myself to simply exist in the comfort of my physical limitations and low self-esteem.

I think back on all the times I felt I had been dealt all the winning cards in my life and with the wave of a hand everything was gone: My family, my health, my career, and my wealth... all gone.

In my youngest of years I experienced the loss of the life of an extremely close friend. It was learned he had sat quietly and patiently in our midst, in a crowded parking lot at a favorite dance club, waiting for the right moment. None of us were aware of the depths of his depression until we heard the gunshot. He had held his precious life in his hand and in a second put the gun to his head, pulled the trigger and died instantly. So few people could understand what desperation could drive a person to this end....Only many years later did I have the misfortune to learn such desperation. It came to me at a time when I had little spirituality, and my earthly life could no longer sustain my needs.

Contemplating suicide can give you a perspective on life that could never be possible otherwise. You become fearless, realizing that death is the endpoint. From this perspective there is absolutely *nothing* left to lose.

* * * *

In the past I have felt undeserving from the Higher Power due to the abusive manner in which I had lived the precious life that had been given me. Yet in moments of stillness, there was always a small voice that whispered *"The best is yet to come!"* Many times it is not a lack of faith that does not bring our desires. Instead, it is a lack of *patience*, which in the end is really a lack of *belief* that we can have what we desire.

When I began to feel worthiness, more of the healing process began. That same small voice which had scolded me in the past now whispered *"God wants you well!"* This became my mantra with the passing of time.

I believe that my chronic fatigue disorder classes existed because those suffering with CF were told its cause "was all in their head" and that there was no physical cure for what ailed them. These women had no other recourse. We live much of our lives based upon input from others. Believing that what we are told, what we read, and what we are taught *is **truth***, while ignoring some of our most valuable assets: *common sense, inner wisdom,* and *practical judgment*. Life becomes so stifled and limiting when we live by the words of others. And of course we have a strong tendency to remain in the rut in which we then find ourselves. After all, the only person who likes change is a baby in need of a clean diaper! But trust me, change can be both wonderfully liberating and painless.

While holding meetings in my home for chronic fatigue sufferers, I also learned that *real* power comes from humility and meekness in the service of others. This was also a factor in my desire to get well. When my brain began to clear and I was able to start helping others is when I began to see even more significant improvement.

* * * *

During my many years of rehabilitation there was a neuropsychologist by the name of Dr. James Quinlan, who would come to my home for my weekly sessions. He would bring lunch, as there was never much nourishment in my environment. After eating, we would sit and smoke cigarette after cigarette as he planted seeds of hope and ideas of how I would resume a semblance of the life I had once lived. *Of course* the conversation contributed immeasurably more to my recovery than did the chain-smoking! After I attended one of the weekend retreats he offered which was to help bring me out of my depression, I decided to thoroughly investigate the role nutrition played in health and recovery. I was beginning to be inspired by the more healthful diet served on these retreats, versus what I was preparing for myself.

The time to take action was *now*. I decided to investigate my options. After speaking with Mrs. Miller, who was a knowledgeable professor from the local junior college, I was convinced I needed to register for a nutrition class offered through the nursing program. I explained to her that my attendance would be subject to certain conditions: My fragile ego could not handle the exposure of my 8th-grade IQ. I would ask to be allowed just to be in attendance, not to be called upon or tested. In addition, there would be no grading or other judging of my ability.

The object was solely to be present in class and hopefully learn anything that would move me forward.

Mrs. Miller was an excellent teacher using a wonderful textbook in her class. I'd like to explain how I coped with some of the challenges I had when attending school. If the information was present in the text I would underline what had been said in class, always making a written note of the page and paragraph number(s) relevant to the spoken material. Since I was unable to keep up with the instructor speaking, I would return to the material later, on my own time, when it could receive my undivided attention. In any case, I just loved those days in class; it made me feel worthwhile even if I had retained nothing from the class. Actually, I not only got through the course somehow, I even received an "A for Excellence"!

I felt sure I had received it merely on the basis of my well-prepared homework, which was basically copying from the text. My desire not to receive any sympathy for my condition led me to confront Mrs. Miller regarding my grade. She replied that I truly deserved the "A" I had received, because my contribution to the class was very valuable and my participation was appreciated.

* * * *

The moral here is to make a conscious decision to remain steady regardless of any delays, setbacks, or disappointments. Never allow yourself the luxury of self-pity — chase it away when you feel it approaching. Either replace it with a grateful thought or think about how much worse the situation could have been. When I could not retain anything I had learned and began to feel sorry for myself, the mental picture of being blind or deaf came into my mind. I would imagine what it would be like not being able to read the textbook or hear the teacher speak.

How did it feel to you as you read those words? Think about it, feel it, remember it — and when you come face to face with any kind of roadblock, *think yourself through it*. This is a situation which happens quite often.

Depression has become rampant these days due to multiple nutritional deficiencies, among other things.

* * * *

My newfound learning was so life-changing! Now I had a plan which would be the center to which I would attach all else. I was becoming obsessed with my new nutritional knowledge, and this included no more weekly Saturday night pizza rituals. My then husband was having great difficulty adjusting to the dietary changes I was incorporating into our daily routine. The need for me to be selfish at this time, whether or not others understood, was of top priority. Other people will accept or tolerate what you do as long as it does not encroach upon them, changing *their* lifestyle.

My self-confidence was a prized possession. I had always known and felt that if anything was my desire, I would find the way to it, if only through sheer stubbornness. At this time my self-confidence was at an all-time low, though I did maintain my stubbornness. And now I had determined that it would be put to real advantage, both for myself and for the good of others who also had found themselves adrift on a sea of helplessness and hopelessness.

4

LET FOOD BE YOUR MEDICINE

Sometimes I would accompany my husband on sales calls in our capacities as insurance representatives. It was a challenging time for me because, as mentioned earlier, I sometimes lost my balance and fell to the ground. In these instances, both the size of the steps I took and the amount of time I spent free-standing were minuscule! One day we had an appointment with a lovely older couple, who were very cordial to us. The woman, who was confined to a wheelchair, dominated the conversation somewhat as she and her husband proceeded to take control of the visit. They were just as anxious to share their story with us as we were to make our sales presentation to them. She told us how she had eventually become bedridden with a severe case of multiple sclerosis.

In the course of my life when I saw various sicknesses and diseases around me, my mind would proceed to categorize them in terms of the degree of seriousness and severity. This sales call was one of those times. Employing knowledge I had gained from my college classes, I compared this woman's situation with my own and realized that they were quite similar. Both of us had disorders of the nervous system — the difference being that I had been damaged physically. But in spite of the differences in our conditions, her story was giving me a glimmer of expectancy regarding my own situation.

Up to this time, my experimentation with health and diet supplements had resulted in very little improvement in my condition. But what I was about to experience was unlike anything I had ever had before. It was a drink consisting of live fruits, vegetables, and herbs in a powdered form. She said to think of this as if they had just been picked from the garden.

"Would you like to purchase some of these food supplements?" my husband respectfully asked. My initial response was to decline. I remember thinking at the time that I had had the very best drugs in the world and all sorts of supplements, with no success. Why would this "grass" make any difference? The woman began to explain regeneration versus degeneration, and spoke of self-repair on a cellular level. At this point I became more candid in voicing my opinion. She respectfully expressed sympathy for my distressing situation, as her own condition had gone on for so many years. She explained that there had been no real progress in her condition until she had made a change in her diet and added supplementation.

My husband's last comment to me was "You have nothing to lose." Those were exactly the words I needed to hear at that moment — because the moment would have passed and good health would have been lost to me forever. Instinctively I thought to myself, "If I do not take this opportunity now, where will I be next year and the years after?" So far, I had utilized my stubbornness — now I needed to address my impatience, with which I had struggled all my life. I knew exploring this option would be no quick fix.

God bless the broken roads that lead us to our destinations!

* * * *

So I decided to become immersed in the journey, for which I was developing a strong motivation: Evidence from research led me to realize I was then going through a rapid progression of aging — *degeneration*. For at the end of the day, what are we but *cells* dying and rebuilding and becoming either more sickly or more healthy with each successive generation?

As I followed this new plan for improved health, it was a period in which I really had to question myself.

First, did I really believe I was **nourishing** my body as was necessary to have great health? Could I really eat enough excellent food to make a difference, when much of the nutrients and energy from what I ate was used to beat my heart, work my lungs, etc.? This in addition to digestion, which in itself would use up most of the energy derived from the healthful food eaten — that is assuming I could find healthful foods. With all these bodily demands, this would leave very little for the repair and healing of my body. And what about the penance to be paid, to make amends for all the damage and abuse I had laid upon my body in previous years?

Through this succession of questioning and answering, I was convinced that eating a variety of nutritional herbs could possibly provide missing components needed for my recovery.

With time, I came to believe that *sickness is really **the body hungering** for specific types of food.*

Secondly, was I **cleansing** the systems of my body sufficiently on all those days and sometimes *weeks* when I did not eliminate properly? Which begs the question, "Was I *ever* really eliminating properly?" Well, your guess would be as good as mine. I had stool that looked in appearance as though Roger Rabbit had snuck into my washroom when I was not looking and made a deposit into the commode.

Surely the most important factor in keeping your body working as intended is your elimination habits. Without the "plumbing" working efficiently, everything becomes polluted and, indeed, "poisoned" over time.

I have since learned that blood moves through your circulatory system every twenty-three seconds to nourish and cleanse the cells of your body. *My* blood was being "fortified" with nicotine, caffeine, sugar, fat, and at times alcohol. Not knowing this at the time, I never gave a thought to the residues left in my body by the substances I had ingested. This is comparable to the accumulating ash produced by the burning of coal in a furnace. The ashes would accumulate and slowly the furnace, the body's metabolism, would be dampened — and could eventually die out.

* * * *

Within the first couple of weeks, I began to notice subtle improvements. I remember telling my husband that I felt a kind of *awakening* in my body that I had never experienced in the past: having the energy to get farther through the day before tiring, in spite of chronic fatigue. I was experiencing the beginnings of a night's sleep which left me more rested the following day. A slight but noticeable change to the unexplained bruising and the superficial healing of skin abrasions, as well as less inflammation of my psoriasis....

Including other things as time went on — such as changes to the appearance and the development of various symptoms, and yet never realizing these are experiences we should not be having in our day-to-day living. We are accustomed to seeing people around us experiencing many of the same issues. Therefore we begin to view this as "normalcy", and no individual or group has told us this is NOT normalcy.

Allow me, if you will, to enumerate several more of these changes in no particular order. My migraine headaches seemed less severe and less frequent, after having experienced them without relief for many years. The nightly nightmares were becoming more of a vague memory. Experiencing a more relaxed sleep, I began to rise incrementally earlier, feeling more refreshed. Although I still continued to take naps in the afternoon, they were shorter in length.

No longer was I shutting out the world by turning off the phone, closing the window blinds and not answering the door. My frequent mood swings, which would range from deep hopelessness to anger and hostility, found less of a home in my emotions.

My feet, which had shrunk to the extra narrow shoe width of AA, would ache from painful bunions, calluses, and plantar warts. Their soles were painful to the touch. I now found it possible to wear shoes for a longer time and to walk a further distance. My knees (both of which had been broken in the past), troublesome while walking, now seemed more flexible along with other various broken bones I had accumulated thus far during my lifetime. Aches and pains, in addition to muscle cramping and other symptoms of fibromyalgia which had only worsened in the past, now improved.

The indigestion and heartburn — the latter sometimes so severe that my throat would be burned raw — from which I suffered included constant bloating, frequently accompanied by gas pains. This bloating, together with my thin and frail appearance because I wore a dress size of "0" (zero) at this time, made me appear even more malnourished. Sometimes my tongue would swell, making speaking difficult. This condition gradually got better — and I began to glimpse some meat on my skeletal frame, along with having a bit more strength. My fingernails would split and peel, and there was always a more-than-normal shedding of hair from my head. These had not yet stopped, but they had showed positive change. Likewise, the amount of gray hair on my head had also lessened.

My teeth had loosened; my gums were sore and would bleed when brushing my teeth. Ever since the accident, I would grind my teeth so severely at night that they had begun to loosen as a result of the bone in my jaw breaking down.

Now, my mouth was feeling much more comfortable, my breath became sweeter upon awakening, and the swelling of my tongue was diminishing. After eating I felt less of a "stuffy nose", which felt like a shortening of breath. When I woke in the morning, my eyes and eyelashes would feel as if they had been glued together with a kind of hardened "crustiness" during the night; this also improved.

These conditions were the topics I studied and researched. I learned that these were caused by *deficiencies*, which could be remedied easily. Contrast this with various doctors' opinions in the past: that either I was simply aging and that was the reason for my appearing to be falling apart, or the explanation that some people are simply cursed with weaknesses of their heredity.

* * * *

But more than just a catalogue of symptoms, there were the irritations, inconveniences, and trials added to my daily existence. For example, for years I had had a ringing in my ears, and a kind of rustling sound intruded upon my hearing — especially when I tilted my head to one side or when I lay down. Various shapes floating in front of my eyes were a daily occurrence; at times my vision would be so clouded and blurred that my prescription glasses would not help. As mentioned earlier, driving was not really permitted to me as I could lose my way when driving less than two blocks from home. There was no memory or ability to visualize routes I had previously taken. And when I did ride in a car at night, I could barely see due to the fuzziness the lights caused to my vision. These things *did* begin to change, but it took time.

It was these frequent, unexpected malfunctions of my body that made life very torturous. One by one the frequency and severity of each of these became less — beginning with a dread of sleep which forced me to continuously relive the car crash. I would wake with a tingling and numbness in my arms; then it was off to the Gonstead Clinic in Mount Horeb, Wisconsin for a week of chiropractic treatment to relieve these physical expressions of the stresses of body and mind for another three months. After following my new regimen, the tingling and numbness began to subside, along with the sciatica which had plagued me for many years before the occurrence of the car accident.

* * * *

I have always believed that cleanliness of body was a priority; this from the days when I was a model — an activity in which one is in extreme proximity to others. *I had never felt **truly** clean until the time these changes began in my body.*

I was troubled by a constant body odor which may not have been obvious to others, though noticeable to myself. There was a constant discharge from my personal area and from my underarms, which felt as though they had a coating which could not be totally cleansed. My interest in sexual activity had become completely void; as my former husband could verify, sexuality was the last thought on my mind....

And people today wonder why they have little or no interest in sexuality — or have *no spirituality* — when their brains as well as their bodies are laden down with unhealthy substances and pollutants, and from unhealthy activities as well as unhealthy thinking. The manner and thoughts by which your mind processes information *dramatically* affect the way you feel about *absolutely everything* in your life. There is not the smallest issue that is not touched with great impact by your attitude.

I began viewing those around me with a new presence of mind, feeling as though I had discovered a *"sacred treasure"* holding the keys to *anti-aging* and above-average health with the body's built-in instincts at the helm, navigating myself (and eventually others) to good health as I had never, ever, before experienced. Sometimes I was engulfed by a feeling of gratitude and a sense of obligation to share this discovery with as many people as possible, in order to free them from their addictions and questionable lifestyle choices — which, quite simply, are the bases of the lives of many sick and dying individuals. As previously noted, I have been there, where they are, during my dark days of chronic fatigue and fibromyalgia: living for a period of time by eating candy and drinking sugary drinks and coffee, all the while smoking cigarettes.

Change can happen without much discomfort when done in a gradual lifestyle adjustment. Equally as important, there must be something *new* to begin when something *old* is ceased or is removed.

5

PTSD? ANXIETY? DEPRESSION?

Throughout my life I have observed that most people would rather shut the door on the unpleasantries of life rather than walk through it and face them. Now the appropriate time had arrived, and I was gathering up the resolve to walk through that door and face those buried, painful memories. My attempts at keeping the door shut were becoming futile. My subconscious mind had chosen to bring me messages through my dreams.

This brings to mind occasions on which I had inquired of several doctors, specializing in disorders of the mind, whether or not the subconscious mind also lost *its* memories in the same manner as the conscious mind.

None of them were ever able to answer that question. So I will answer it for them. I believe the subconscious carries on just as it had previously. Also, I believe it may take a little time for it to present itself once again.

Greedily, I embraced one of the most important facts I had ever learned: *"Nothing in life is permanent, not even death!"* — because there *is* life after death. Upon waking in the morning, this thought would be racing through my mind. Just as the eddies of a stream are constantly changing, so are the patterns of our existence. Once again I allowed myself to think about my diagnosis, this time with a different attitude. When I had been told I had severe cognitive impairment, with an 8th-grade IQ and PTSD (Post-Traumatic Stress Disorder), I felt very uninformed in regards to the details but too ill to care. None of the medical professionals who treated me at that time actually explained to me what I could expect, and how PTSD would impact me for the rest of my life.

Eventually, the ability to comprehend started to return; I was able to do a little research and to understand what had been happening to me all these years.

If I may, I would like to attempt to explain this to you as I understood it. PTSD is a psychiatric disorder that can result from an accident, a natural disaster such as a hurricane or a tornado, wars, or even a terrorist attack. The memory of the event becomes an obsession.

Up until that time I had been left to my own distorted imagination in wondering what was to become of me. For years I carried the impression that I was slowly and permanently losing control of my faculties. *And then I began glimpsing moments of clarity.* The ability to think my thoughts through was not returning as quickly as I would have liked, but it certainly was being consistent in its return. When a person experiences such an emotional assault, the mind is constantly preoccupied with these thoughts, whether awake or even in slumber. In my case I was traumatized, both physically and mentally, by a series of nightmares which took place almost nightly. The reliving of the car crash during the night became so vivid that it forced me to leap from the bed tangled in bed sheets and blankets, thereby hurling my body to the floor and at times injuring myself.

To this day I have no conscious memory as to whether my eyes actually viewed the crash at the instant it occurred. I can only recall being wakened from a state of unconsciousness by the first people to arrive at the scene of the accident. Nevertheless, there were two "scenes" that were often replayed in my dreams during that time: The first included the sound of breaking glass and the screeching of metal; the second was the vision of my waking in the passenger's seat with my head down and blood pouring down my face from a hole in my head (head wounds bleed profusely), a bloody broken nose and part of my cheek ripped away. I could still envision my once pink blouse totally saturated in the color red.

With the added diagnoses of chronic fatigue and fibromyalgia, I slept almost the entire day yet never felt rested. My emotions were always rubbed raw, and bursting into tears over nothing became commonplace. In fact, whenever I would think about what had happened I would cry, and it occupied my mind almost constantly. I was in denial of the entire incident for the longest time. Anger could occur without any provocation, and it was always unexpected. If anyone had told me that the mind could instantly become panicked enough to turn to thoughts of suicide just to escape the mental anguish, I never would have believed it.

And then there were the *outside* stimuli. While watching unpleasantries on television shows or news reports I could become extremely unsettled, causing actual physical distress. These shows could act as a catalyst, catapulting me back to being trapped in my car — along with feelings of helplessness, fear, and even horror. No longer was I simply an observer but instead an emotionally active participant replaying the same frightening emotions over and over.

Trauma such as this, with actual physical damage along with a psychiatric disorder, actually changes the brain's biology and the manner in which memories are perceived. At least this was *my* experience. There were no earlier memories for me to draw from, no memories of who I once was. People told me I had been gregarious, full of life, and always surrounded by new acquaintances wherever I traveled. In my profession as an insurance agent I traveled a lot and met many. Had those memories of who I once was surfaced, I am confident I would have felt deeper despair and a heavier heart.

Note: Before the body can properly heal, we must recognize that there is nothing more crucial than the "Healing of the Heart." I believe this is the only way to rid ourselves of destructive emotions such as depression, discouragement, hopelessness, and even unforgiveness.

The fact that no one, including my husband, could understand *WHY* I was so different had become a real annoyance. *WHY* I had actually become antisocial and even withdrawn was a mystery to him. I could never expect others to understand—after all, most people have never been close to death. I should have died several times in the past and because of this, change was imperative in order to live and fulfill my destiny.

This is about the time I began convincing myself, sometimes moment to moment, that I would live with positive expectancy. Whenever I had a thought, I wrote it on little cards or notepads or whatever else was handy. I would tell myself repeatedly: "Within me lies intelligence and strength, ready to be used." I would say this over and over, until the thought became stronger than what I was seeing or feeling in the physical world.

The Lord will perfect that which concerns me.
— Psalm 138:8

My mother died suffering with Alzheimer's disease. These were the times when I thought about the stages of her disease and how she retreated into her own mind. I believe her fall into dementia happened because she was no longer needed by her children and grandchildren as she once was. I made the decision, years ago, that mother's final years would not be a foreshadowing of my own. If I had been viewed as an "incomplete woman" in the opinion of others because I did not have a child, then so be it. *I* found that I enjoyed being a single person. I have nurtured more people than have hundreds of women put together. I do not believe, therefore, that a few additional children will change the world, but *I believe that what I do in the Name of Jesus is changing the world.*

My mother's and my illnesses were so very different, yet I had often been told that with each head injury (and I had had two) the probability of developing her disease increased drastically. I felt I had been living in a blur all these years — then all at once everything became different and my world was shifting. I realized I had a choice: believe what I was told, or believe that I could control my own destiny. My mother had no choice; her mind was just about gone. In my case I still had a choice, even though previously the thought of retreating permanently from the world had over time become more and more appealing to me, for all the reasons mentioned above. And only in hitting the bottom did I remember there was a top.

Only recently did I come to realize the most valuable lesson she had ever taught me — how I could get along in life without her and be independent.

* * * *

I recall the meetings I attended for sufferers of PTSD. Those meetings were thoroughly depressing: Unfortunate people feeding off each other's hopelessness and despair, "finding comfort through the discomfort of others." For me it was not a healthy atmosphere. I believe these meetings fostered self-pity. When you render up control over your emotions, **fear** will be the dominant emotion. **Fear** is contagious; it can spread among people as though it were a wildfire raging out of control.

In the midst of my personal depression, many psychiatric doctors had their interpretation of my state of mind: the definition of depression being "hatred turned inward". In my opinion this was felt by many who were attending these meetings. To me, it simply served as another breeding ground for growing even deeper depression — mingling among the depressed.

Self-incrimination never takes us anywhere, except further down into the well called hopelessness. Self-pity, coming from people who are already feeling sorry for their unexpected dilemmas life had heaped on them, can also be fatal to themselves and to others in more ways than one. Most fatal is forming the preeminent mindset that their situation is permanent.

Confidence to overcome any unfavorable circumstances can be gained with every tiny step forward that you take, as long as you are willing to look **fear** directly in the eye, even with the knowledge that you are **afraid**. I am mindful of a verse from the Bible: **"For the thing I feared has come upon me, and what**

I dreaded has happened to me" (Job 3:25). After my injury I lived in a state of fear of lack of money, of aging, of depending on others, and of lack of love. Having lost my ability to support myself, my expectations led to this thinking and I was receiving and living a life which was exactly as I feared it would be. I was challenged to change my thinking, for a positive outcome.

When unpleasant memories are actually seen for what they are, "just memories", they began to lose their power to control your destiny!

I knew the surety that I needed to take a decisive step, or I would take no step at all. And that is exactly what I did when I withdrew from the PTSD weekly meetings. I am convinced that the health of the people you spend time with dictates the quality of your health mentally, physically, and above all spiritually.

Most importantly, I had become resigned to accepting the reality that the damage had already been done in that accident, and now I would need to deal with its results. If I had continued with the meetings, it would have deepened my hopelessness and helplessness, and led to no good end. Now I was in possession of a better understanding of my situation, one which took me years to arrive at. At this time I wish to reiterate once again: It took facing the memories and allowing the pain to be felt in order to go forward. I found that facing the pain will not hurt you....After I began feeling the memories, I asked myself what would be the worst outcome of this situation. It was quite simple. Being dead. Yes, it was death, and I was alive. I was still limping physically and mentally and spiritually, but still alive.

In our lifetimes we are continuously journeying. Many times the specific destination of our journey may be unknown to us.

However, the direction of my path was now indisputable. My energies would be directed toward the rectification of my accumulated damages. I would be willing to open the door and walk through, even if I had to walk on coals of fire to get to the other side and make right that which had gone so very wrong. I could only envision the horrendous challenges...the degree of my cognitive brain damage, for one. This also was about the time I began fighting with my own feelings: I felt unworthiness I felt unworthiness to expect fine health when I took a mental inventory on how my life had been lived. I then took the comparison of two people, both having incurred the same damage. The first one cared for his health and the second one abused it. At this point there was nothing more to think about. The duration of my self-pity was over. I had gotten what I had deserved, and nothing or no one else was to blame.

This is an important bit of information for you who are reading these words. In this life you never know when something will be thrust upon you and you will need all the power humanly possible to enable you to carry that burden. And that is also when we must be willing to both *accept and embrace* our role in whatever unwanted circumstance occurs to us. Because upon looking deeply enough, we will recognize the part we played.

I moved through *my* life with the gusto of a marathon runner. Never did I take time to replenish or restore what was being taken from me by the deprivation of adequate sleep, exercise, nutrition, and the renewal of my soul. These long-term deficiencies, combined with the poisoning of every cell of my body through the habit of smoking (originating from age 13), would now take center stage.

And *center stage* was becoming quite crowded with the "cast of the past" together with the "cast of the present". The cast was composed of every violent act my being had ever received, and *now* it had become magnified. Thinking about the habits I had cultivated over the years, it was plain that there were no resources from which to draw.

* * * *

I began seeking knowledge about health wherever possible. I found college courses in nutrition, offered within a nursing program. For my needs, the classes I attended were limited in content but they were enough to encourage me to continue further along the path of *natural healing*. Traditional medicine and treatment had *not* worked to my benefit; instead, they had led me deeper into hopelessness and depression.

The fog was lifting as I began to see further into my future. I investigated what type of practitioner could offer some actual, tangible healing. A situation in which a person could be involved in his or her own cure, without the use of any type of medicine, even medicinal herbs (which are the source of some medicines).

It should be mentioned at this point that there are three types of herbs: *poisonous, medicinal,* and *food grade*.

I decided that I would avoid any medicinal herbs. Instead, my approach to healing would be through the use of *food grade herbs*. I accepted that this would take a longer period of time to permanently heal than the use of the other, but instead of targeting isolated symptoms, these would act upon the entire body, strengthening its weaknesses. As for my depression, I would forgo the Prozac and instead replenish the material my nervous system needed to make its own happy chemicals.

After investigating the available options, I chose the route of Naturopathy because my research showed that it was the true *natural* path to wellness (and ultimately it was the only way by which I became well). With this in mind, I searched for a school which would be accredited and approved by the American Naturopathic Medical Association. My intention at the time was not to become a doctor of any sort; only to gather the offered knowledge for my own physical, mental and emotional improvement. As mentioned previously, when your life is on the line you have to become focused, which can sometimes be interpreted as selfishness on your part!

Having chosen the mode of healing and the institution from which I could learn, the next issue would be the question of time leeway allotted to complete the course-work, graduate, and become certified. Certainly I would require an extension, which I requested and which was graciously granted.

Another concern on my part was the matter of contacting various influential people who could give me a character reference. This worried me for a time, because it was as if I had dropped off the face of the earth for many years. *What could those people now say on my behalf at this time?* But, as I will continue to repeatedly demonstrate, if something is your destiny all obstacles will be taken away — such as this one.

* * * *

Learning the material presented in the courses, and what was required to pass them, was very valuable to me. The thought occurred to me that my personal experience of illness, disease, and injury would be even more valuable to me for the purpose of turning back the clock physiologically — my goal was the *repair, revival, renewal,* and *restoration* of the strong constitution which I felt inherent in me from a very young age. Again, the reason for obtaining a degree was not actually to put it into a health practice, but to gain new, valuable knowledge which would be of great use to me in the rebuilding of my self-confidence — regardless of the outcome of my attempt.

From the time I began this program of studies, I was spending an inordinate amount of time speaking to teachers in an attempt to sort out confusion in lesson material. Due to the accident, I had had quite a bit of damage to the cognitive learning center of the brain, by which we are able to perceive or process concepts. I often felt that the information was in my brain; it just was not within my comprehension at the time.

Did I feel stupid? *You better believe it!* I was always in an apologetic frame of mind, as well as being verbally apologetic, due to my inability sometimes to grasp what was being *said, read,* or even *thought.* When I was undergoing rehabilitation, the instructor would use "flash cards" for me to relearn basic addition. I had difficulty arriving at the correct answer for the simple sum of "2+2": I knew very well that 2+2 was 4, but I was unable to understand how I would arrive at that answer. Although I was diagnosed with an 8th-grade IQ, to me it felt more comparable to that of a 2nd-grader's intellect. At that time I began recalling the words "See Spot run", contained in my 2nd-grade reader. Ironically, this is how I came to choose the name of my first website, SEEDRLEE. COM, lest I forget where I came from!

All the same, when I am tempted to think about all I had lost (firstly, a lucrative career), I thank God for His mercy. As I wrote this at 5:15 a.m. this morning, I asked God to keep my arrogance in check. The answer I received, a whisper in my mind, felt heartwarming. "Without that arrogance, we would not be sitting here having this conversation!" — Meaning, I feel, that *without* that arrogance I simply would not have had the belief that I could get myself well!

* * * *

As I was getting into my third year of studies, I was questioning whether I would actually accomplish what I had set out to do. My learning was progressing so slowly that at times it would come to a complete halt, as I could not handle the stress of managing my now undisciplined brain. My emotional ups and downs made it difficult to apply myself continuously to the task at hand. I found myself constantly petitioning God to give me the strength to persevere. So often it seemed that I was just going through the motions of learning, but in the end finding myself holding onto *nothing* after hours of study. However, during this time one thing that could not be denied was that I was a living laboratory for testing the validity of various modalities of recovery, based upon the practical results they achieved.

I feel confident in saying that this could be confirmed by my former husband and in-laws, who questioned the *sanity* of my actions.

Then a completely unprompted telephone call came from a school counselor. The situation was somewhat bizarre because not only had we never spoken before, but she professed that she never made telephone calls to students! It so happened, she said, that while reviewing various files that morning she was compelled to read mine. Thus she became acquainted with my learning difficulties. She then said that she had been bothered the rest of that morning by an insistent urge to make this phone call to me, and that she would have no peace in the progress of her day had she not. She proceeded to designate herself as my personal tutor, available to me as needed. Once again I had found, seemingly from out of nowhere, essential aid for me to progress further in my studies.

Too often we are dissatisfied because we haven't arrived at our destination. **Good heath is a journey, *not* a destination. It cannot be captured; it must be pursued. And it must be pursued consistently and continuously for the desired benefit.**

Now, I have no idea what you may be thinking at this moment, but my conclusion about this matter is that this was truly a Divine Intervention, not an earthly coincidence! In my life, I've seen Goodness (a euphemism for God) directing my eyes and attention towards whatever my need might be at the time. It has never been necessary to seek or search, because needed aid always seemed to be made available.

The Chinese have a proverb, "When the student is ready, the teacher will appear". Is that not appropriate? They also have a saying that all journeys begin with the first step, and this first step will be the most profound for us both. Although I knew I had not yet arrived at my destination, I was on the right path. No longer was I viewing the pursuit of my goals as winning or losing, moving forward or falling back. My focus was only that I was "back in the game".

"What game?" you may ask. To that I would answer, "The most consequential game of my life". On the 16th of July, 1997, I completed the requisite course of study leading to the degree of Doctor of Naturopathy, which was awarded to me with honors.

6

TO THE FAR EAST: THERE & BACK

Another decision of some consequence was about to present itself. Of course, our lives are all about making decisions on *everything*, ranging in magnitude from the trivial to the life-altering. If I was sincere about challenging the degree of improvement in my condition which I had achieved to date, here was an opportunity! It was a trip, a very long trip, to the Far East.

Up until this time, I did not realize that I had embraced my physical injuries like a warm coat wrapped around me on a cold winter's day. This would not be a pleasure trip. Instead, I was told it would be a learning experience and have a degree of travel that could be very grueling physically. It was a trip which would lead all the way to Beijing, China! Moving about on this trip would be totally dependent on my body's strength and energy reserves, as there would not be much time for rest.

Being unable to navigate in these unfamiliar surroundings would force me to keep going and keep up with my fellow travelers, who like me were there to learn and explore.

In this case, the learning would be uniquely based upon Chinese tradition. Realizing that to date my ongoing journey to good health had not taken me far from home, I felt — unconsciously if nothing else — that perhaps it was time for me to expand my horizons. There was *so much more to learn*, and I had already gotten such a late start on learning, that there was no time to waste. For example, some of the important information to be gathered was more about attitude and balance, rather than about feelings and disease.

After my introduction to the existence of supplemental food-grade herbs in 1991, I became somewhat obsessed with the pursuit of knowledge pertaining to a philosophy which existed and evolved over 5,000 years ago, and yet was almost a kind of "sacred secret," understood and practiced by so few compared to the world's population.

The word "regeneration" is almost never referenced in the Western medical world, only the word "degeneration". Dictionaries define regeneration: be rebuilt, be restored, be recreated; and my favorite, be spiritually reborn. Degeneration is just the opposite of these. I believe regeneration is exactly what is being accomplished in my life and is constantly ongoing.

Very simply, if your lifestyle habits have you walking on the edge of a cliff, you are risking all that you are and all that you could ever be. And I walked on the edge of that cliff almost my entire life, believing that a fall would never happen to me. But it did, and it broke my body and my mind, as well as my spirit. I lost everything — with the exception of God. As I write these lines, I pray for you right now that this will never happen in your lifetime.

I feel sure you understand why, even though I was somewhat unprepared, when some years later an opportunity to travel abroad to the Far East presented itself I leaped at it. Not only did I wish to truly and deeply understand with my recovering mind all that was both earthly and spiritually possible, but I also saw the opportunity to test my recovery, in order that I might keep improving and therefore look forward to the improvement of others as well.

* * * *

There was a marvelous sense of freedom which I felt during this period of travel. It refreshed my mind through the making of new memories. I would be carrying none of the baggage that had previously weighed me down.

As our flight descended to the runway at Beijing airport, we were greeted angrily by a typhoon. On a scale of 1 to 10, with 10 being the strongest, this violent tropical cyclone measured an 8. Residents and visitors alike were giving their utmost attention to a storm of this magnitude.

My mind was racing and my heart pounding in my chest as we made our way down a heavily-sheltered walkway leading us into the airport terminal. Midway down the ramp, the question flashed through my mind: Had I come all this way after all these years of health challenges, only to be swept away by one of the most violent storms ever endured by man — a so-called act of God? With the completion of the question a most indescribable sense of peace came over me as the response to the question entered my mind: "Child, this is only the beginning." Now there was no fear, only an appreciation of God's sense of humor and of the ways He tests us.

When arriving at the hotel, you could feel the controlled panic of those around you. In horror, I looked out the hotel window at the shop owners, the flooded streets, and the pedestrians struggling as the waters rapidly approached an adult's waist-level. I thought about the Chinese people and their resilience. I felt this was neither the first nor the last time they would see such destruction, and I experienced mixed emotions watching their businesses washed away in what seemed like an instant. They would begin again, I was told, as they always had in the past, from the ground up.

Thoughts about the similarity of our losses — *their* losing their material possessions and *my* losing the ability to utilize my mind — went much further beyond being merely inspirational: They led to the thought that both could be regained.

Ralph Waldo Emerson said: "Great men are they who see that spiritual is stronger than any material force, that thoughts rule the world."

* * * *

Many experiences at this time were intangible — though to me they were priceless. At this point I would like to attempt to describe an "awakening" that touched my very soul.

Previously I felt as though I had been locked against my will in a dark room for many years. When suddenly, the door opened and I stepped out of the dark into the light. The warmth of the memory of *being truly alive* was returning to every cell of my body and my mind. This was my first conscious realization that emotions really do change your biological chemistry — for good or bad.

Shakespeare, that amazing mind, observed that "there is nothing either good or bad, except for thinking makes it so."

This warmth of being alive in mind and body made me more receptive and giving to the multiple people who had gathered in China from around the world. My vision of myself was changing. No longer was I that physically fragile, brain-damaged, disabled person. With my new friends in China I was a new person. Specifically, my new acquaintances, who quickly became friends of both myself and my traveling companion. Ron Bevil and Richard Czimer did not view me as that easily broken individual. It was similar to a rebirth—but this was a rebirth of a rebirth, which served to remind me of my self-worth and long-forgotten self-confidence. They unknowingly gave me both emotional and physical assistance as needed on this trip. You could say they gave me reinforcement of what I always believed, which is that *"I am more than capable."*

I recall that at the trip's end we had missed a connecting flight which would return us to the United States. This would prove to be quite challenging, due to the eight different broken bones I had encountered in my lifetime, in addition to fibromyalgia and the need to take to my bed for many hours of the day in past years. Each one of us was forced to individually carry our own bulky luggage, which was even more laden and weighed down with our new purchases. I had no choice—I was forced to keep up with my companions or be left behind. The frantic pace with which we had to sprint down the walkways was now more burdensome than I could have imagined, *but I did it!* As the four of us continued to run, they also continued to reassure me that I was physically capable in spite of my pain and discomfort. Once again, God provided me with exactly *what* was needed and exactly *when* I needed it.

Einstein said "Coincidence is God's way of remaining anonymous." Isn't that the truth!

❋ ❋ ❋ ❋

There was much to be savored and relished upon my return from my China trip. China was a true testing ground. Aside from this, it was my good fortune there to meet an aged Chinese physician. During one conversation he had related to me that at this time my personal compass was pointing in the most favorable direction. He was very forthcoming with the fact that I would continue to heal and could become a great healer if I were able to exercise self-discipline and control in my own lifestyle habits.

"So you should determine to reach that goal by completely changing your diet; *eat what you should eat and stop eating what you should not.*" Being a great doctor, he knew that I had lived an extremely undisciplined life. In my mind health and healing had become so complex. But there it was: His words had humbled me when I made the comparison to what I thought I knew.

As I took the lengthy plane ride back to the United States, leaving an entirely different world behind, I pondered the conversation between the doctor and myself, imagining what it would be like to be *truly healthy* and not to be in possession of anything at all that could debilitate me throughout my life.

As noted previously, something or someone always came within view when I least expected it, enabling me to continue on my life's journey. Here, thousands of miles from home on this trip, I met people who not only became my friends almost immediately; they changed my life. I shall be forever grateful to Ron and Richard, who helped me remember my own self-worth.

In a word, one might say they woke me from my slumber. I have found that there are such individuals who, with just their sheer presence, can radiate all the physical and emotional support needed by another.

* * * *

During my return home to the United States I was accompanied by a positive vision of my future. Great peace in my heart had returned with me as well, which I vowed to maintain. In order to implement my resolve, clearly my life would have to change from what it had been in the past. For the first time since the accident I was becoming my own person — somewhat fearless and certainly directed.

I made a decision to work towards removing myself from the dependency of permanent disability. I felt that would be a necessary step — no more training wheels! And I continued to hold to the belief that God had saved me from my past in order that I might share hope and faith with others.

Optimism, my constant companion and which had helped me to maintain my sanity, also opened the door to another life-changing decision: Regardless of the cost, *I needed a free and clear mind in order to pursue my goals for myself and others*, with no one standing in my way.

My marriage was over. The life my husband and I had attempted to build together had begun to self-destruct many years before. Illness and injury will inevitably change both a person and those around him or her. It is impossible to go through either of these unscathed. As I reminisced over the path that we had gone down together and how our own paths had diverged over time, I felt confident about my need to once again be single. However, there was and is no refuge from the pain of memory and remorse, even when viewing the prospect as a positive change.

Surely, it would require the Divine Intervention of a Higher Power for me to afford a lifestyle alteration of this magnitude, given my current financial situation. Living on $880 per month and charging purchases to a handful of credit cards, I would return to the home I owned before my marriage. It took great courage for me to be brutally honest with myself regarding the situation—as well as to depart from my shared home with nothing but the clothes on my back and those in my closet!

Changes—even those for the betterment of all—are never without complications and can escalate rapidly into major difficulties if one lets one's emotions gain the upper hand. Through it all I became cognizant that it is not so important where we have been, but more importantly, where we are going. Lesson to be learned here: Never look back; it will keep you from feeling regret. We need to bury the dead, not carry them with us.

This is the time in which I would take stock of what I thought my life would be and what my life still could be. Now, in my mind's eye I began to see a picture of a healer—tentative, but nevertheless that of a healer. Would others see this same vision of me? That would be the most important question to be answered. And where would the answer come from? I guess we will have to wait and see.

* * * *

At about this time I was given the opportunity to have a lovely office at St. Joseph's Medical Clinic in Lockport, Illinois.

This opportunity would be provided by a doctor, an M.D. He would often engage me in conversation as to how I would handle various cases he himself was treating. The conversation always came around to the same question: "Would I take this patient off of his or her prescription drugs?" My reply to him was always the same: "No. I would solve the mystery of their illness, and YOU would then take them off their prescription." The good doctor always laughed at my reply. Sad to say, he had a serious case of diabetes and he felt that I could not do any more for him than he was already doing for himself. He passed away from complications not long after.

When I left St. Joseph Medical Clinic I sought other rental space for my business office. At this time I was very much alone, having lost most living relatives. Through circumstances, I was fortunate to have the friendship of Tony and Carol Doszak, my earthly guardian angels. Seemingly they were always there when support was needed. Tony and I went to view the space. It was as if I were following a compass, and that compass led me to Larkin Avenue in Joliet and to the acquaintance of Dr. Amin and Hazami Kater, who have continued to be two of the most generous, honorable, and understanding people I've ever been privileged to meet. When my office was needed some years later for a lab, the Katers actually created a space for me in the building next door, a project which included a new private washroom.

After finding this quaint little office, I happened to visit a patient in a local hospital who had a "staph" (staphylococcus) infection. Previously I had fallen on a patch of ice at a nursing home and broken my elbow. Due to the break's severity several pins were required to rejoin the bones, requiring me to wear a full cast which left me unable to drive. The resultant time was used to visit several people in the hospital. As previously mentioned, a woman had had a staph infection but authorities assured me that the bacteria were totally gone from the environment.

Knowing the virulence of this particular infection, I should have never believed them and never entered the room. For, the next day I had a raging infection in my elbow.

Soon the cast was taken off, but the doctor and I agreed that the pins not be removed until the infection could be eliminated. The $129.00 antibiotic I was given was used up in two weeks, after which time the infection came back with a vengeance. With the help of a friend who visited me daily, we used compresses made of crushed fresh grapes, placing them on the elbow in order to draw out the infection. Fearing the contagious nature of the staph infection during this period, I ultimately stayed out of my newly-rented office for months. The infection disappeared, my arm healed, and the pins were successfully removed. The doctor attending my case was excellent, but he told me that he could not guarantee the results because I had refused *more* drugs. My own feeling was that I had given the prescription drug route its chance. This natural method took longer, but it was safer and more permanent.

During this period it was as though an epidemic was raging within my immediate family. The name of this epidemic was *cancer*. Brain cancer. Prostate cancer. Lung cancer. One year after the other, each more horrifying than the last. At this point no one in my family wanted my help; they chose to be treated in the conventional manner, using chemotherapy and radiation. This was understandable. However, the missing link was *nutritional support*, if only to build their immunity. The exception was my youngest brother, who suffered from a brain tumor. He was given a death sentence, allowing him a mere three additional months to live after his brain surgery. Concluding my own assessment, I felt that his defenses could be rebuilt. However, his doctors were confident that he would absolutely not survive beyond the estimated period. Therefore they had decided not to remove the entire tumor because this would impede his motor skills, speech, etc.; even so, their decision would not be decisive as to whether he *actually* would have the ability to walk and talk during his last days....

I remember the day I went to his house and asked him if I could help him, using the discoveries I had made in working to put my own physical house back in order. "Yes", he answered simply. "What have I got to lose? I have been given only three months to live." These were my own words, echoing back to me: *"What have I got to lose?"*

Thus the challenge began. Soon my brother moved to a care center. At that point, as he lost the use of his limbs and the strength to lift anything, his body was no longer at his disposal. I was almost like a reliable clock, daily revealing the hour as I arrived to give him various supplements. His physical strength and mental capability improved as time progressed. Together we changed his death sentence of three months to live into a reprieve of five and a half years!

My plan was to get him strong enough to remove him from the care center into my home and employ someone to care for him when I would be at my office. Unfortunately, by this time the cast on my broken elbow left me unable to drive myself to the care center to provide him with his supplements. Meanwhile, someone having legal power over his care had insisted that by Doctor's order, nothing was to be brought in from the outside by way of supplementation. After explaining the situation to my brother, I assured him that if he wished, I would pursue and fight for his rights. Answering me, he gratefully acknowledged all that I had done for him — in essence giving him over five years beyond what he could ever have expected without my intervention. Three months later, I quietly and stoically sat in a room watching as my baby brother slipped into a coma and passed away.

7

SETBACKS & COMEBACKS

By this time I was feeling quite well; my elbow had healed fully, and I was ready to resume my health practice in my new office.

I had made multiple errors in the beginning. Having needed great discipline and perseverance to get to where I am in improving my own health, it took some time for me to realize that others were not willing to be as conscientious and devoted to *their own* improvement. Primarily, this is because others' lives have merely been "interrupted" by illness — they have not been told (as in my case) "*life* as you have known it *is over*".

Experience has taught me about human nature, and how to *nurture* rather than *oppose* nature.

At the beginning of my practice, the approach I used with my clients was identical to that which I had put myself through. However, this approach was not proving to be the most successful with others. In my diet, for instance, I eliminated almost everything but vegetables, meat, and fish. It turned out to be too much to expect others to be able to abstain in this manner. My own diet regimen was followed out of sheer desperation. Except for a few clients who came into the office suffering from cancer or severe heart trouble, others simply did not share the desperation that drove me.

I remember one client, a man who had liver cancer and needed a liver transplant. He suffered from cirrhosis of the liver and hepatitis as well. His original doctors gave him no hope of being able to strengthen his body enough to undergo the transplant. He was so ill he was unable to come to the office for his appointment. Instead, his family filled in for him, giving me the required information I needed for his case. Although he was on various drugs, I had no fear in taking the same approach I had taken with any other person with a weakened immunity. My faith was strong — strong enough for those with little or no faith of their own. In my imagination, I saw him *completely well*; he would live to enjoy the large family he had engendered.

What occurred next was that one or more of his drug dosages were set too high and he was rushed to the hospital. Ready or not, the decision was made for him to undergo his liver transplant surgery at that time. I still treasure the letter in my file written by his wife, expressing her appreciation for her husband's undergoing a successful transplant.

Maybe I was too naive back then to be frightened of what was taking place, or perhaps my faith was simply *unrelenting*. Whatever the reason, it had all worked out beautifully: This was one of those situations with a family who fully supported each other, doing exactly what I had asked of them. This has not always been the case, however.

Then there are those times when perhaps fear or indecision can prevent a person from completely surrendering to a new approach to healthcare. I look humorously at these situations. I picture a person who has one foot in Eastern medicine while still leaving one foot in Western medicine. I truly understand this; it can sometimes be confusing and somewhat overwhelming to make a different choice.

Jo Anne's story, below, is representative of what can happen when a person is not forthcoming regarding the medicine(s) she continues taking after seeking care from another doctor. I invite you to follow along with her in her futile pursuit of health:

> Back in 2001 I was having much difficulty just functioning. I went to Dr. Wickes and was checked for breathing problems; in 2002 I went to Dr. Pundaleeka and had a test run for hemochromatosis. In 2003 it was confirmed that I have the hereditary hemochromatosis. On October 31, 2003 I was denied gastro-bypass surgery from the University of Chicago even though I had been diagnosed with diabetes and was over 100 pounds overweight, but was denied on the grounds that I wasn't a repeat dieter. In 2004 I went to the sleep clinic on September 1 and again on October 16. In 2005, on January 10, I went to Peaceful Nites in Joliet [Illinois] and was diagnosed with a sleep disorder and provided a CPAP machine [used to treat sleep apnea and ease breathing — Lee]. In 2008 I had a cortisone shot in my right foot for arthritis at Hinsdale [Illinois] Orthopedics, and after testing was to take Prevacid according to Dr. Girgis of Hinsdale. In 2009 one of my doctors recommended Actonel for me, and another doctor said I should not take it. In February of 2009 I went to Sherin Lee in Joliet,

Illinois, with all the same complaints. While seeing Sherin and doing as told (for the most part) I changed my eating, but I had also been going to an endocrinologist and was still taking medication. Sherin never ever told me to stop any medications. This was not the problem. The problem was that I failed to share this information with her. She explained that not having complete knowledge could affect the manner in which she proceeded, and that in turn would affect my progress.

—Jo Anne Furbee

* * * *

I believe very strongly in the **power of** *fasting*—so strongly that this subject was a major focus of study for my Naturopathic degree. There are many varieties of fasts, depending on the circumstance and the need. If I may, let me define my reasoning. There is much misunderstanding and misdirection regarding fasting. A *metamorphosis* occurs during a fast. At this time there is a tearing down and rebuilding of damaged materials. Fasting dissolves *diseased* cells in a systemic manner, never disturbing healthy cells, tissue, or muscle. Animals fast when they are sick or injured. When we are unwell our appetite diminishes; and yet the Western world still insists upon force-feeding the ill, never allowing the body to build up the energy to heal and squandering that energy on the task of digestion.

There are many negative stories about fasting. Fasting is a science in itself. To me, this simply means that the assistance of an experienced health care provider is necessary for a successful fast.

"Fasting is the greatest remedy, the physician within."

—**Paracelsus**

(Paracelsus was a 16th century Swiss physician who pioneered an external cause for illness and the use of chemical remedies.)

To the contrary, in my experience I have noticed a link between eating too much of the unhealthy foods and the increase in high mortality in our society. Paul C. Bragg, ND, Ph.D., and lifestyle authority, took the position that average people are poisoning themselves unknowingly each day with the food choices they make. They are doing so by never questioning whether a food is healthy or harmful, as long as it looks appealing. Few know the correct foods to keep them healthy.

With regard to the many breast cancer conditions I have worked with, it is puzzling to me that this disease has continued its spiraling increase, while occurrences of other diseases have been greatly reduced and some totally eliminated.

Throughout my life I have been generous with all types of worthy charities, although I have never been prompted to give to the cancer society. After my bouts with cancer and the deaths of numerous relatives, instinct tells me that the cause is not to be found in a test tube and neither is the cure. We say we are only human; this does not have to mean we are weak. We can make the decision by controlling what foods we ingest, what we breathe, what we put on our bodies, and most importantly *what we think and speak over our bodies*. What we need to control is not in the world; instead, *it is within us*. Sadly, my other family members died from their cancers; but I survived mine, never to return again, and that to me speaks louder than my words ever could.

As mentioned previously, it is my belief that the *emotions* must be healed initially (the "Healing of the Heart") — even more so than the physical conditions. Recalling my own experience with cancer, my life at that time was both turbulent and emotional.

[Allow me to mention here that I was married to a most wonderful man at that time, who totally supported me in my recovery — Richard Lakotic (whose modeling name is Jason Richards).]

There has always been a part of me that believes my "stinking thinking" and debilitating lifestyle resulted in my developing leukemia when in my 20's. It was not just "bad luck". Prior to developing cancer, earlier in my life my liver was extremely inefficient, as well as harboring *a lot* of anger. I believe that emotions are stored in the liver.

Early in my practice, the situation of one woman was extremely painful emotionally. Many times, issues are so deep-seated we are unaware they even exist until we can begin to purge them. This was so in this woman's situation. She had buried so many painful and bitter feelings, attitudes, and emotions that she almost could not face them when they began to surface.

In the beginning she had had great success in her healing. But when people are no longer fearful, their demeanor changes and they conduct themselves differently. They lose that conscientiousness and attention to detail that they exhibited when they were in *fear*. In this case it was imperative that her strength return very, very slowly, so as not to feed the remaining cancerous cells. Unfortunately people dismiss their internal condition and instead place emphasis on their exterior appearance as noticed by themselves or others. This is exactly what happened. Her emphasis was placed on the body's external appearance in spite of the serious warning given her. She allowed herself to accept the opinions of doctors with no understanding of natural healing. Because my warnings were ignored, and by following others' advice, unfortunately the cancer returned.

This was an occasion where I would not go through the healing process again with her. I have given people multiple chances, where they have failed to follow my instructions. Once a person contradicts my advice **of great importance** which can mean **life or death**, I may suggest they find another healthcare provider . Frankly, I question whether they can be trusted going forward. Trust between people is imperative when taking a healing journey together.

* * * *

As time went on, I began to better understand how people conduct themselves when they are not well. Knowledge of this can explain so many of the ways in which individuals disappoint, hurt, anger, discourage, dismiss, misuse, and abuse other human beings. In living my own life I have come to experience many of the events of unease and despair lived by others. Looking back on all those occasions, I am thrilled by the idea that I was chosen to have such experiences for the sake and betterment of other people. To know the anguish, pain, desperation, and finally the joy when events come to a successful outcome is greater than the satisfactions received from any other avenues I have traveled.

* * * *

Allow me to say a few words at this time regarding reasons people do not heal. Let me suggest some reasons which may have prevented or retarded *my own* healing, since from time to time I myself have experienced some of these causes.

For some who are chronically ill, I believe their illness fills a very real, essential, psychological and emotional need. It gives them a sense of security that their lifestyle structure will remain the same. Remaining ill insures that there will be no surprises in their lives. There will be no additional or varied discomfort, which often accompanies change. And above all else, it proves to be a specific, effective template for bringing attention to oneself — attention that one may not have otherwise received, or may even have been totally missing in one's life. They become a special person. Some will embrace a feeling of hopelessness, wearing it like a badge of honor to show the world. When I identify this as a barrier to healing, I am going to a deeper level — one concerned with self-esteem and sheer worthiness. *Change can be frightening.*

Courage is not the absence of fear.... Quite the opposite, it's taking action in spite of fear.

There have been instances I have witnessed, some personal, some professional, in which grown men were fearful regarding whether or not they would be capable of again resuming responsibilities, providing necessary income, etc. for themselves and their families, should they get well. In this instance it is not so much a matter of self-esteem as it is one of self-confidence and fear of failure.

There is also a laziness that tends to creep in over a period of time. Everyone likes to be comfortable; above all else, striving for leisure time. However, too often in these cases the person's life unfortunately ends up being mostly just that, leisure. This in turn leads to a person lacking in direction and accountability and dependability. This scenario was very familiar to me. During my own illnesses it required force in order to NOT choose the easiest way.

It is not my belief that all illness is the result of tragedy; and so it was in my case. Ironically, I am *thankful* for the misfortunes resulting from my car accident, including the brain damage I incurred. The reason? With all the injuries and accidents which happened in my life to that point, *nothing was being learned.*

However, when my mind (which included memory, will, and determination) was taken from me by that accident, *I became open.* My condition then might be looked upon as having been a kind of physical guide, leading to real insight, learning, understanding, and finally acceptance of the deeper meaning of life. And could not each of us say that, sometime or another, we have learned a valuable lesson or lessons from some misfortune? It is especially so when forced upon us, like some nasty-tasting medicine we tend to remember longer.

Various research shows that approximately 87 percent of illness is attributed to our thought life. Negative emotions can ruin your life physically and mentally. Approximately 13 percent is due to environment, diet, and genetics.

Another reason people do not heal can be that a person's energy level is actually being drained through a fear of standing apart from the crowd. They may be shown a lack of respect by stepping out of the so-called normal and accepted channels of healthcare treatment. There are times when we find ourselves swimming against the tide: when we may be forced to actually give up opposing relationships in which the other person is not understanding or supportive of our healthcare choices. This latter situation can and will conclusively hinder our recovery. No matter how lonely it becomes — and for me it was very lonely — one should not allow oneself to wallow in that loneliness. In my own situation, I instead immersed myself in the visualization of wholeness, balance, and happiness. Sometimes when others forsake you through a lack of support, even mustering a seed of faith can be difficult. Although the good news is that, if you wait for even a few minutes, the winds will change direction once again.

* * * *

I have had an immense amount of physical pain in my lifetime. Never having been one to seek or use pain medication, I would treat the pain through my mental attitude. I never saw the experience as my enemy. Instead, I would treat it as my messenger, a messenger telling me something needed my specific attention. This would cause me to look deeper and become more aware of how I was treating my body at that time. Coincidence? I think not.... As mentioned previously, our thoughts powerfully influence the health of our minds and bodies, affecting us at the very core of the healing process!

There are times in which the basis for illness is *not* physical, mental, or emotional; it can be environmental. As such, it can sneak up on us so slowly and stealthily that we never see it coming. On the other hand, it may be blatantly obvious, yet we never take the time to notice it. For me the environmental bases of my illness would be smoking, eating fatty foods, getting insufficient sleep, being in smoke-laden surroundings, and a total lack of nutritious foods in my diet.

Given a body burdened by such an extreme constellation of factors, it will take a focused and extremely strong willpower to assist it to rebuild its damaged, diseased, and dying tissues. In the face of such a huge task, this is the moment to stop focusing on weaknesses and instead celebrate your strengths and your willingness to recognize the necessity of change. This, I believe, can be your very first step to exuberant health!

I truly believe that anyone can be made strong from any weakness that presents itself. Most importantly, that person must first believe it in his or her own heart. After they visualize their wellness with their eyes closed, it is necessary to constantly revisit each detail of recovery. Of course it is normal to sometimes receive one or more severe setbacks on the journey to wellness. This is the time when you *must* hold on to hope!

A person who cannot grasp the belief, the hope, that he or she can be well, will face a continuous conflict and an unrest of spirit. In these cases I focus much more attention on *my* belief system, in which case I am carrying hope for both of us. I believe that whatever we *think about* — and especially whatever we *thank about* — we *bring about*.

And we all know that we are never thankful for the negatives that befall us. Ironically, I've discovered that these are the times to really be thankful! Think back. For the most part, did they not teach you a much-needed lesson? Sometimes it takes a crisis to wake us. However, that crisis may make a person fearful. That *fear* can be infectious around you and within you. This is where you need a sound base, something larger than yourself to seize and hold dearly to your heart.

Feel the fear, and replace it with hope.

8

THE DECISION: I CAN AND I WILL

A s you might have surmised by now, it took several long years to arrive at the point where I could direct my thoughts. In fact, to many it would have appeared as the obvious beginning of the end. Surprisingly, it was the start of a new and better beginning. The fulfillment of the promises of God has come alive from my favorite Bible verse: **"Beloved, I wish above all things that you prosper and be in health, just as your soul prospers" (3 John 1:2).** For many years I conveniently selected and focused on the promise of prosperity and ignored the rest. This means that I put no priority on the health of my body, or the health of my soul. In my life, when I felt unworthy and least deserving is when I was *most* worthy and *most* deserving.

Big or small, sick or poor, sinner or saint: We are all worthy to receive the promises of God — and let no one tell you otherwise. At this moment it seems strange even to be able to write the written word, let alone to quote the Bible verse above. For many years I could barely sign my name legibly, and most certainly could not remember anyone's promise to me — especially the promises of God. Although my opinion of myself has at times been too inflated, this pride, false or real, has kept me from *ever* seeing myself as a failure. When life knocks me down, I am always more than willing to get back up!

Never think for a moment that I have not been fearful, but I am not afraid of fear. It takes being willing to commit to the words "I can" and "I will"! It is a succession of your proper actions which can be applicable to almost every challenge of life.

It had taken a conscious decision not to dwell on what was being seen in the natural world around me. A conscious decision to ignore what I felt and especially what I was hearing from others. However, this did force me to ask myself this question many times: "Could I overcome these disabilities and become well, when everyone else believed I never would?"

Could I succeed in overcoming the "handicapped" label placed on me by others?

I imagine I was satisfied with an 8th-grade IQ when I was in the 8th grade. But would my mind accept this prognosis decades later?

After wrestling with these speculations, the obvious answer was that I had fought too hard my entire life to give up, lie down, and play dead. *There is always a choice.* If these questions had been tossed to the side every time they had surfaced, I would have sat on the fence forever. This means never going forward, but most definitely going backward!

When faced with a challenge, the five simple words I ask are: *"What is there to lose?"* Really think about it deeply and consider it carefully: It may be just what is needed to move you forward. For me this question always removes the clouds of doubt from my view. After all, remaining in doubt is undoubtedly making a profound decision, whether we want to acknowledge this or not! And in doing so, we become and remain a kind of paralytic, deadened to the situation. One can never possibly possess that which one never pursues.

When injury had forced me back into having the mind of a child and I was in the midst of all this physical and mental chaos, I'd lay quietly just as I had when I truly was that child, listening to the birds chirping outside my bedroom window. They were so close and yet I never looked at them. I visualized them mining the ground for worms. And, one particular morning this vision impelled me to another thought: God places countless worms throughout the world for the nourishment of the innumerable birds. Never once to my knowledge has He EVER placed the worm into the mouth of a bird. There it was. The profound truth, not the false doctrine taught to me my entire life.

I was taught and stuck believing that I should pray and plead with God for my wishes, and if I were a good girl who was worthy, I may receive. This false belief could have held me captive for the rest of my life. Thankfully, the truth was exposed in that moment. Why did I ever believe that the Son of God would suffer unmercifully, die for me, and NOT include my sickness as well as the inclusion of my sins? He always knew I was unworthy and always would be. In the doctrine I was taught, no one would ever receive God's promises because no one would ever prove worthy.

To return to the birds, obviously I was not mining for worms; but just as the worms were made available to the birds, so also was healing made available for us all.

I personally was missing important details when praying; and then I made a most valuable discovery.

It was found in **Matthew 17:20** (and I paraphrase in part): **"For truly I say to you, if you have faith the size of a mustard seed you can say to this mountain, 'Be thrown into the sea,' and it will be if you believe."**...I learned that it was *my responsibility* to speak out loud to *my* mountains, and have the faith that I could throw them into the sea. And most importantly, that my faith need be only the size of a mustard seed to be effective.

Never had I even thought of speaking to our personal mountain(s) — that is, commanding my maladies to leave my body. Instead, I had continued to plead with God, not recognizing that I already had received the gift of healing. There was a second and equally important step that needed to be taken, one that would be equally as challenging as the first:

BELIEVING you have received, BEFORE YOU CAN SEE ANY PROOF, requires some real, special effort!

When your spirit awakens you to the many truths in life, embrace these truths. Make them a part of you. Put them in your heart and allow no one to steal them from you. Grasp these truths, hold them tightly, refuse to let go. But be aware that you will hear, see, and even feel contradictions to your beliefs. This is when I have told myself, "My strength is of the strength of ten, because my heart is pure."

I learned it is not the delays, interruptions, setbacks, or even the stalls. Instead, it is that you are willing to begin, and how that will propel you and allow you to feel about yourself in the end.

Had I received a miraculous healing it would have been simpler, and oh-so-awe-inspiring to myself and others — although I am convinced that in my situation and in many others there is always much more to experience and to learn along the way to healing. The fact that understanding and learning from my experience would aid and inspire others helped me to remain patient on this journey more times than I care to remember. On many occasions I spoke positive words out loud: "I CAN AND I WILL."

However, equal power has been given to the words "I can't"....

Life gives us the rewards of our actions. You reap in harvest either success or failure: Projecting either of these beliefs will absolutely and powerfully determine your destiny!

It took additional years for me to become cognizant of the repressive words which I had been speaking over another area of my life. This came about for a couple of reasons.

Having been told that I had the IQ of an 8th-grader and that I would never be able to learn or work again, I chose not to embrace such a prediction. I expected that there would be some hurdles to jump. My chronic fatigue was slowly departing, although there were still days when appointments would be canceled or rescheduled due to migraine headaches, or not having the energy to dress or drive to the office. And there was the time spent in rehabilitation, poorly relearning basic mathematics skills from 1st-grade-level flash cards — skills which still left a considerable challenge in my day-to-day financial activities.

Making childlike mistakes when interacting with others proved to be quite embarrassing. Most commonly, these were errors which occurred when adding fees or when products were sold. A calculator was still too complicated for me, so I knew I had to suffer through it to get better.

In the meantime there was financial loss to myself, in the office and at the bank. It was a continuous pattern. Sometimes twice a month I would fail to add or subtract properly and be charged for bouncing checks and insufficient funds.

In the past I strove for excellent credit and a somewhat sterling reputation for reliability in financial matters. Now, I had to accept the fact that I was presenting a very negative impression among those who were once my peers.

While I was making my way through the remains of the greatest upheaval of my life, I was thankful that my creditors trusted me enough through previous years to give me large lines of credit. However, no matter how secure some situations appear, the tide can always turn against you. At this point in my life, there were no relatives or good friends left. It was **I** in the big, deep, dark waters — and it was sink or swim!

During this period of time a close friend had created a website for me. Having no knowledge of its workings, the website went down for almost two years. Never having gone to the website or grasped an understanding of its importance, my business came to a screeching halt. Of course this was a tremendous setback, though I could not take too much blame for I did not understand the technology, nor at that point had I ever spent one moment on a computer.

People do not understand what it is like to return to the world with half your brain cells being asleep. After some years

I was forced to do so by a friend, Barb Burk, who purchased a computer on which I could learn the basics of its use. Previously I could use the reasoning that I could not afford it, or had no one to teach me — both frail excuses in the eyes of another. It took years to remember the sequence for getting into my e-mail. I must tell you that I was extremely proud of myself when I finally did. It was a battle I fought with both hands, because just the thought of opening the computer's cover overwhelmed me.

Most difficult was overcoming the skepticism of people who have no knowledge or experience regarding the type of healthcare methods I offer. The words that others had often told me repeatedly echoed through my consciousness — that no one would seek the alternative healthcare I was offering. In my mind, this was the only method that would truly reverse others' chronic or acute disease. It was naiveté that caused me to believe that everyone would want to experience the degree of wellness I had acquired. Call it naiveté or call it foolishness, but it has been proven over time that it is only for a select few, broad-minded individuals who are willing to take the care of their health into their own hands. At this time I was becoming discouraged by my lack of progress. Financially this was an extremely lean period for me, as well as a time of rejection.

Fortune smiled on me along the way and I made the acquaintance of an exceptional chiropractor, Dr. Timothy Radcliffe of Lockport, Illinois. I was the fortunate beneficiary of his knowledgeable guidance as a healthcare provider. He prodded me with guilt, telling me that I could not quit, as I owed my knowledge and expertise to a world where so many were in need of healing.

Viewing my life through someone else's perspective helped me to come to terms with issues about which I had vacillated for a great many years.

* * * *

Many people simply fear natural medicine because of a lack of understanding. Many others want no responsibility for their health, and assign that task to another person—which in this case allows them to blame someone else when the outcome is not favorable for them. And still others just are unaware of the fact that they have other healthcare options.

Here is where I believe we have to become critical thinkers. By becoming educated and being taught both sides of a subject, only then can we make informed decisions. Let me explain further by telling this story. During the period of time I received government disability payments, it was mandatory that I visit a Medical Physician for an extensive examination on a regular basis. During those times the doctor would order a complete blood profile.

Improvements in my health were seen in my blood test long before the rebirth of healthy, new brain cells was identified. The doctor was amazed when the results of these tests were returned for reading. Finally, her curiosity got the best of her and she finally asked what I could possibly be doing that could result in such dramatic improvements in test after test.

Years of being entrenched in medical training and drug therapy had made her a skeptic, and her mind could not accept that the use of food-grade herbs could actually regenerate a person's health to the degree proven by my tests. For example, for many years I had a low-grade infection and severe anemia. This was reflected by blood tests which showed a very high white blood count and a low red blood count. As I improved my immunity, my blood count normalized. I educated the doctor on my regimen, but she still was experiencing disbelief and told me that she needed to think about it. It was understandable that, tempted as she was, she would not give in. After all, if *Allopathy* — Western medicine — could not get me well, it would be the highest insult that *Naturopathy*, Eastern medicine, would restore my health, and right before her very eyes!

If we close our minds, maintaining only a small glimpse of the big picture, this will affect and limit our choice of options. In other words, just because you do not see a way does not mean that there is no way! There are also others who are followers of what is mainstream and do not want to be identified as being different. Embrace the fact that God made you special, with freedom of choice. Now, be willing to make these choices and to not care about the opinions of others. Sincerity and dedication will not get you where you wish to go if you are traveling on the wrong road!

If I desire my life to be different, I must not only think and speak differently, but my thoughts and desires have to be bigger than I myself believe possible. It was realizing that nothing limited achievement like my own small thinking and the utilization of only that of which I was capable. At my weakest moments, I saw myself as minuscule against a world of giants. For example, on the subject of finances: Pleased only to have enough money to pay monthly bills, with that mentality that is exactly what I received, and many times not even that much. Again, I quote: **"Beloved, I wish above all things that you prosper and be in health, just as your soul prospers" (3 John 1:2).** What do these words mean to you? Does that mean that we should not want or expect more? After my accident, I expected so little — *and I received even less.*

Cut free of those self-imposed thoughts, and those opinions and labels imposed by others. Throw them on a pile, light an imaginary match, set fire to them and watch them burn! Unhappy, unpleasant, false memories will only have the life you continue to give them. Get all the false beliefs in order, so they can be shot down one by one like dominoes falling. When I came to *accept* that I was alone in the natural world, I also came to realize that I had everything I needed in the *spiritual* world — *where all true power exists*. I believed that God wanted me well and that I would heal. Very simply, many do not heal because they have no belief that they *can* heal.

But my journey did not begin with faith and belief; instead it began with a ray of hope. It grew into optimism as my life progressed. No longer was I trying to build more faith; instead I began working on lowering my *un*belief.

It takes great discipline to speak words of faith when your heart is in doubt and your mind is possessed by unbelief. It is possible and quite common to be in both faith ("that it *can* happen") and unbelief ("that it *will not* happen") simultaneously. *Simply force your heart to have less unbelief!*

* * * *

As you continued reading this book, you would have noticed that certain ideas and suggestions have been repeated.

Repetition was my one best friend. There was a need for repeated positive reinforcement. So, let us declare victory over our lives in detail: *"I am healthy, strong, and getting better and better in every way!"* Whenever I was asked how I was, I would deny myself the luxury of complaining. Instead, I would proclaim: *"I am better!"* — no matter how I really felt.

Strongholds in your mind can get in the way of you reaching your ultimate destination. This is why it is necessary to establish what is the truth and what you are willing to believe. Make it in the present. The mind knows only the present; it does not recognize the future of things to come. I took some of the most beneficial beliefs and elaborated on them: Thoughts such as *"God wants me well"*. And telling myself that it is never too late to change. I believed that *"the time is now"*, with NO setbacks, delays, interruptions, hesitations or exclusions. No longer would I look for *change* in the future, because it *exists only in the present.*

I stopped taking my complaints to God. I took responsibility, commanding my body to heal. Even to this very day, when I stand praying I believe I have received.

* * * *

My health and the health of others have been my passion for several years. I am of the belief that our passion is an induction of what God has planned for us.

Most people I have known do not consider the possibility that all things, good or bad, exist for a higher purpose. It becomes labeled good luck or bad luck, good fortune or misfortune. I would enjoy telling you a story showing you a different slant on a sad outcome. Like me, anyone can become a permanent slave to disease, lack, loneliness, or depression. My wish was to become free of these encumbrances, but I also wanted others to be free, as in the case of my youngest brother. Setting the stage for such lessons, God took my darkest hour and made it my most valuable turning point.

As previously mentioned, my brother Rob was diagnosed with a brain tumor and given three months to live. Had someone not interfered, I am confident that he would still be alive today. Had I completed my plans of getting him well enough to come and live with me at my residence, you would not be reading this book because it would never have been written. My time would have been dedicated to the care of my brother and to a part-time health practice.

One of the saddest days of my life was an Easter Sunday when I was housebound, due to a cast on a broken elbow along with a staphylococcus infection. It was necessary to isolate myself from others just in case. Unable to drive a vehicle or leave home, I was having great difficulty accepting an order placed on my brother's chart at the nursing home. The order read that I was no longer allowed to bring supplementation for his healthcare. He and I discussed the situation and he thanked me for allowing him to live longer than he expected. A short time later he went into a coma and died.

It took time to understand and accept this turn of events. When I removed myself from this picture and looked again, I will tell you how it changed: *With my brother's removal from my life I would fulfill the plan God had laid out for it.* How did my brother fit into this picture? *God used Robbie to show me that no matter how hopeless the prognosis, anyone can be healed.*

If you believe in God, you will also believe He will remove any obstacles and that it will always be for a higher purpose. Even though we have free will, I believe our lives have been planned out from the time we were in our mother's womb. I therefore hold to the belief that no one life was designed to end in failure. Something deep down inside me was revealed to me: that this was not the way my story was to end. Lonely, and broke.

Who better to write about sin but the sinner? Who better to warn you than one who has been there, and most valuable of all, returned? I've fought mediocrity my entire life, always wanting to be above average, with the exception of health. It did not seem important; therefore it took no priority. I took it for granted instead, being too arrogant to believe I could ever lose my health.

When I recognized I had my priorities all backwards: This is when I would prove that I was not average and I would reverse every burden that had ever been placed on my body, mind, and spirit — and make it a blessing in having had the experience.

The moral being, whatever belief and desire we hold in our thoughts is what we will manifest if we are consistent, no matter how impossible it appears. Looking for God in all my mess is when I was shown the miracle. Many people put the words of the Bible on the shelf along with the Bible. I put the words of God's promises in my heart. In my having received the mercy and grace of God, I feel almost desperate to share that grace with the rest of you. We usually want to give what we have been given — as in forgiveness. We must forgive because we have been forgiven.

These are the battles that are won or lost in the mind. That is exactly the reason why *we need to become enlightened with God's promises and put them in our hearts*, where they will always remain and be retrievable when needed!

Oftentimes I express thankfulness for the extreme turbulence I have experienced in the waters of life. Only as the waters deepened did I see greater wonders. Only when I became suicidal, thought I would surely "drown" by taking my own life, and was about to give up, did I feel God's hand reaching in and placing me on dry land. And once again giving me a new hope.

I have since learned that you do not have to be or have the best of everything. Once I began to make the best of what I have, I began to have more of what I want. Just like in the Bible and the story of Job, I lost my health, my family, my business, and my possessions. As of this writing, my entire life has taken a turn, going upward rather than continually spiraling downwards.

Wishing you health, wealth, and peace!

Graciously,
Dr. ND

APPENDIX

A Gasp, and Then a Breath: Veronica's Story

Veronica's story shows us how God directs our path.

My name is Veronica Rodriguez. I'm writing this to give comfort and hope to anyone who is going through a difficult time in their life; my wish is that they will never lose hope, and always *believe*.

In 2009 I became ill with bronchitis — that was the doctors' diagnosis. They weren't entirely sure what was happening to me, and decided they were going to treat it as asthma because that's what seemed to be working. "Good," I thought. "Everything is going to be fine" — not knowing that it was just the beginning of a three-and-a-half-year struggle.

And not knowing that my life was going to come to a stop, and eventually be transformed for the better.

I had already had some health issues: Most of my life I had been plagued with allergies and sinus problems, but issues with phlegm and feeling "out of breath" developed a couple of years before I became ill. None of these were that bothersome except for the phlegm, which was getting worse, though I never went to the doctor for it. I just didn't think of it as a "big deal", and was too embarrassed that anyone would know I had this "phlegm problem". (It sounds silly now when I think about it.) The phlegm issue was with me constantly, every day, but was not yet severe, so I still refrained from going to the doctor. Eventually, I got sick with what the doctors said was a respiratory infection, and *that's* when it all began — when I ended up in the hospital with a diagnosis of bronchitis.

I was hospitalized a couple of times after that and in and out of a hospital "ER" (emergency room) for treatment numerous times during the following years, and for the same reason: respiratory problems. My life had changed drastically. I couldn't be active at all. I'd be out of breath and exhausted just going up the flight of stairs at home; I'd be done for the day. At times the condition was so severe that it took a lot just to lift a finger or say a word — I'd be that out of breath. On those days I couldn't get out of bed, I'd call on my family for help, since my husband had to go to work and my son David was only four years old at the time. My parents stayed with us off and on to help. I don't know what I would have done without my family at that time.

Every day was unpredictable. On some nights I'd wake up choking and gasping for air, and my husband would call "911" for an ambulance to take me to the hospital's emergency room (one of many trips). I'd be given a steroid shot and I'd make it through once again. During this time I was in "survival mode". On a good day I'd be able to take a shower, make dinner, and maybe do a light chore; but by the end of the day I would be exhausted. Sometimes I'd pay for it the next day (or *days*) or even end up in the hospital emergency room.

It was really hard for me to accept where I was in my life, but eventually I learned to accept it—which made life a little easier.

There were many things I could not do with my little boy, like going for walks to the lake or going bicycle riding, which he loved doing. There were times when he would ask me to read a book to him. I'd start reading and then be out of breath. It was really hard to tell him I couldn't finish reading it, but he was always very understanding. He had become very attached to me during this time. I noticed a change in him—He became more loving and caring towards me and towards others, but I always wondered how all of this would affect him later.

I was finally diagnosed with asthma, sinusitis, and allergies, and was put on six different medications. These didn't help much—at least not enough for me to have a decent life. It was definitely helping me to stay alive, but at the same time I was getting sicker and feeling weaker than ever. For a while I was also getting allergy shots, but these were stopped after I became even more ill. I even had allergic reactions to many of the medications normally given for asthma and allergies. The doctors didn't seem to understand what was going on.

There was never a time that I wanted to go to the emergency room, but many times I never had a choice. I was extremely tired and weak, and didn't know how much more my body could take. And, my experiences in the ER were becoming scary. The staff didn't know what to do with me since my test results were coming back as being "Normal". I never understood this, because at this time X-rays would show that I was having spasms. They only noticed my nasal drip and nasal passages being inflamed but nothing else, when in fact *I felt at times that*

I could stop breathing! I knew something was seriously wrong, and I wasn't going to give up trying to figure it out. I'd tell the ER staff that I needed a steroid shot—I knew it was the only way to help me breathe. One time a doctor prescribed an antibiotic for me; my nurse practitioner then took me off the drug, saying that I didn't need it. I ended up back at the ER the next day, when another doctor put me back on the antibiotic, saying I *did* need it. Many similar situations occurred during this period. One year I went to the hospital emergency room *twelve* times!

My pulmonologist (lung and breathing specialist) had asked me if anything like this had ever happened to me before, which of course it hadn't. He had also mentioned how dangerous steroids were and was concerned that I had been given too many steroid shots in such a short period. I really appreciate everything he did for me, including seeing me so I could avoid a trip to the hospital ER for that particular flare-up of my breathing problem.

I was living a nightmare. Most of the time, I would be O.K. if I wasn't active—meaning that I had to "stay put" and not do a thing! I wasn't able to go places where I had to walk a distance, and so I rarely did so. When I did, I'd walk very slowly and could only walk for about five minutes; then I would take a break to catch my breath.

It was frightening! Sometimes I would leave the store without purchasing all the items I needed because I knew I was running out of breath and that using my inhaler wasn't going to be enough. So visiting my family and friends were my outings because no walking was involved. Even then, there were times that just talking and laughing with them would bring consequences later — but at that moment it didn't matter. I wanted to have *some* enjoyment in my life and forget about my condition, at least for a little while, even if taking a breath was *never* a comfortable experience. If I felt so sick that I couldn't hide it, I would stay away from family and friends — unless I couldn't get out of bed, when I had no choice but to phone and tell them.

I think back now, wondering how I was able to do it, when so many times I really felt that I could die. To have to go on for three years, day after day, without much air was *very* uncomfortable and distressing. How did I ever make it through? I realize now that it was never *my* strength. It was *God's power* working in me all along.

Visiting a friend on one occasion, I was talking and laughing, having a good time — yet all the while I felt very uncomfortable due to a lack of oxygen. I began having trouble getting enough air, but kept going anyway. As soon as I left the house I told my husband to take me to the ER *immediately*, because I was running out of air and needed a breathing treatment. I didn't own a nebulizer (a machine to help you breathe better) at the time, but eventually I bought one and that stopped many of the visits to the ER.

Months later, however, even *that* wasn't helping much anymore, and I became more ill. That's when I began taking steroid pills and shots more often — aside from the six *other* medicines I was taking for asthma and allergies. The time came when steroid *pills* alone weren't enough, and then I often needed a steroid *shot*. I knew the danger of getting them, but I had no choice. It was the only way I could breathe, meaning it was the only way I could stay alive.

It was the only way *at the time*, until I could find *a better way* — which I always believed I would, and never lost hope.

My health was declining rapidly. So I decided to go for a second opinion, to which my doctor agreed. He was questioning if my condition was asthma because he had tried everything to bring it under control, without success. My second opinion didn't go well at all. The doctor I saw then was very close-minded; he made me feel like it was all in my head, then he mentioned that maybe it *was* sinus problems. I brought up the idea of trying acupuncture, and he said he "didn't believe in any of that stuff". I couldn't believe the things he said to me — and neither could I believe this was happening! That was when I decided to turn to alternative medicine and try acupuncture.

During this time I had pretty well hidden from my family and friends how ill I really felt, and didn't talk much about it. All that was visible to them was my phlegm problem, because I constantly had to spit it out. They weren't there to see those times when I could barely walk to the bathroom or get up to feed my son. There were many times I wanted to cry to release my frustration but was unable to, because of a lack of oxygen and the energy it took. So I rarely cried during those years but instead I sought peace; peace, so I would be able to handle my emotions. And it *did* help to keep them under control.

I always had store-bought, prepared food available for David to eat at those times when only he and I were in the house. I also taught him how to dial *"911"* (the phone number for emergencies) on the telephone, so he could call for an ambulance in case anything should happen to me.

I remember a particular time, in my bathroom, not knowing anymore what to think of all this. I was getting tired of trying to stay strong, and felt that I was about to "lose it". I wanted to give up and I envisioned myself throwing everything off the counter and crying, screaming, and falling to the floor, absolutely helpless.

But I refrained from doing it because I was afraid that if I did, I would not be able to "pull myself together". When we let ourselves fall deeper into a hole, it becomes harder to get out. So I talked myself out of it by thinking of God's promises and that I had come too far to give up now. I never did allow myself to "go there". Instead, I tried my best to stay strong and patient, to go through life as best I could. I didn't want to be a burden to anyone, and I didn't want anyone to feel sorry for me.

(Once I got well, however, I was *forced* to go through an emotional stage. I had been holding in so much emotion for such a long time. I could finally let it all out, which was very healing to me.)

We really don't realize how precious our every breath is. How much we *really* need the air we breathe in, just to brush our teeth, lift a finger, or say one word. There were times I felt that I could stop breathing any minute, and in those moments I would be begging God to keep me alive. I've never needed Him more than in those moments when the emergency "911" phone number was called, and every second counted. During this time, I never lost hope and I never stopped believing and having faith in God. I always believed He wanted the best for me. It was the only way I was able to get through all this.

I was doing everything I could to stay strong and positive. In the beginning, I had not been so patient as I was to become later — and of course there were times when I became discouraged and wanted to give up and let go of life. But then I'd see my son's face and couldn't bear not to see it anymore, or how he would be affected if I were to pass on. Everyone else hurting at the time would eventually be "O.K."; but David, he'd be the most affected. So I decided to fight on, and I fought *for him.*

As I mentioned earlier, I had decided to try acupuncture, and I did it for about a year. It was a blessing, and definitely helped for a while. Visits to the hospital ER stopped, and I was off most of my medications. I was still struggling with my illness, but was grateful that I was getting better. I felt the acupuncture was keeping me alive, but after almost a year I started to fall back. My illness worsened again. The last thing I wanted was to relive what I had gone through before; I felt I wouldn't be able to go through *that* again. I felt that God was telling me it was time to look elsewhere.

But I had no idea what to do next. My family was very worried as my illness continued. They decided I should go to the Mayo Clinic in Rochester, Minnesota, and proceeded to make an appointment, but I didn't feel I could make the trip. I was always out-of-breath, and very weak. The thought of getting ready for the trip seemed too much for me. I know they were trying to help, but they couldn't understand my real condition because you couldn't tell how sick I was just by looking at me. And *I* couldn't explain it to them because I didn't have enough breath or energy to do so. Also, I didn't want them to worry. They would panic if they knew that at times I felt I could die. So many thoughts were going through my head. I was so confused.

So I turned to God, telling Him exactly how I felt. I told him I couldn't do it anymore, that I needed Him to do it all for me. I was specific with Him in what I needed: a really good doctor, a doctor who knows exactly what I have, and can resolve it. A doctor located close by, so that I wouldn't be going far.

Then I got silent, and "naturopathic doctor" came into my mind. Although it was always exhausting doing research online, I got on my tablet computer and did an internet search for "really good naturopathic doctor". Dr. Lee's name came up. I checked her website and read her story, and it was pretty amazing. I had a really good feeling about her and felt I needed to call her, so I did. She answered and I briefly explained my problem. I asked her if there was anything natural I could take that would help me immediately; otherwise I was going to the hospital emergency room for a steroid shot. The thought of having more steroid shots was frightening. My body was too weak and I didn't know how much more it could take.

And she answered "Yes, definitely!" I was relieved and willing to try anything she'd tell me to take — I was desperate. So I took what she said and it alleviated my symptoms and it was enough to keep me from going to the hospital ER. She was very sweet and helpful during our phone conversation. I remember her telling me that God wanted the best for me and He wanted me well. When she said that, I had a strong feeling that she was going to be the one to help me, because all this time I too believed God wanted the best for me.

She saw me the very next day. I will never forget that first visit to her office. She was the answer to my prayers. She is an amazing healer. She examined my eyes and was shocked: "You should be dead. I can't believe you are walking around." As she finished her words, an overwhelming presence came over me—God—and He took me back to those moments when I had begged Him to keep me alive, to help me breathe. He revealed to me that very instant that He had been there and answered me in those terrifying and helpless moments---He had saved my life.

Sometimes we don't feel Him, but it doesn't mean He's not there.

I had never felt His presence before. I had no control over my emotions and broke down, crying. And when Dr. Lee gave me a hug after examining me, I felt that it was God who gave it to me. The love I felt from that hug was unbelievable. I can't explain it in words. Months later I learned that when that happens, you have actually met God. I have no doubt that that's what happened that day. The hug was given to me from Him, through her. Since then, I have experienced His presence several times—but never to that magnitude.

After she examined my eyes, she noticed I was having trouble breathing, and my chest was feeling pretty tight and I was having lots of phlegm, as usual. She told me she had this "miracle oil"—that's what she called it, and that's exactly what it was. It opened up my airways and helped me tremendously. I was so excited—I was able to breathe without steroids. She rubbed some on the back of my neck and massaged it. I put some under my tongue and under my nose. Dr. Lee also fixed me some type of tea, which was wonderful. She was very understanding but also very direct and bold. She explained how my diet had a lot to do with me being this sick. She also said, very seriously, that if I didn't watch what I ate, not even she would be able to keep me away from the ER—which was all she needed to say! And that, if I did what she said, I was going to be alright.

Before I met Dr. Lee, Sherin during the time I was ill, I had this strong feeling one day that I was going to meet someone amazing through this. When I met her, I knew she was that person. To this day she still amazes me. She's a very intelligent woman. On that first visit she was able to see right through me. I broke down in tears, which was so unlike me, but she made me feel so comfortable. I felt so relieved to tell someone how I had been feeling all this time, and it felt great to have someone who truly understood what I was going through. Dr. Lee was very understanding because of what she had gone through after her car accident. She gave me a hug and I left her office feeling better, and stronger in my faith in God because of her.

The next morning I felt pretty sick again, so I phoned her and told her that I was tempted to take a steroid pill. Her reply was, "It is always your choice, but if you do, don't bother calling me back again, because this isn't going to work." She then explained why she thought this way. Needless to say, I never got a steroid shot again. She explained that I could use the oil as much as I needed, that it was like my steroid shot.

And so I did exactly that, and I also took the products that she told me to take, which are wonderful. I felt them working right away — my body started to feel stronger. I took them exactly as she asked me to, and I also watched my diet. It was a challenge, but it was worth it! I am no longer on any medications.

Eventually I had to confront my family and go against their decision for me to go to the Mayo Clinic. I had decided to cancel my appointment at the clinic and to stay in town and begin my treatment with Dr. Lee. To this day I don't regret my decision, even though some of my family members didn't agree with it. As much as I appreciated all the help from them, I had to do what

I thought was best for *me*. I needed to listen to God and I felt He was telling me to stay put, that Dr. Lee was going to help me and that I would be alright. Only *I* knew what I had gone through and why I had made that decision — one reason being that I always felt there had to be another way for me to get well without the use of medications.

Now that my health is better, I can't express how joyous I feel. To be able to breathe well is priceless, and enjoying life again feels amazing. *I feel alive!* Regardless of what's going on around us, life is beautiful — God gave it to us; how could it *not* be? We are only here a short time; why not enjoy it as much as we can and not stress over the little things? It's important to our health.

I wouldn't change what happened to me, as difficult as it was. It has made me a better person and I now see life as more beautiful than I ever did. Just the relationship I developed with God as a result was worth it.

I also met some great people, Dr. Lee being one of them. Meeting her has been a great blessing in my life. She is a very interesting, intelligent, elegant, sarcastic, passionate, loving human being — who also happens to be a very strong Christian woman and who loves to be right (and usually is). I've never come across anyone like her; she is a very unique individual. If there is one thing I know for sure, it is that she truly always wants what's best for me and for others. Dr. Lee can be very direct and bold at times, but she is always very encouraging and helpful (and a lot of fun to be around!).

I've learned so much in such a short time, just being around her. I can't say enough — she really is an amazing person!

I am eternally grateful for Dr. Lee giving me my life back. I always believed and had hope, and held on to God's promises — and He came through. He is incredible!

The "Rebirth" of David: Retracing

David is the son of Veronica Rodriguez, who told her story in the previous section. He was also treated by Sherin. This is his story, as related by his mother.

The purpose of this story is to illustrate some astounding, almost miraculous experiences that our bodies go through when cleansing and regenerating. In particular, an unbelievable revelation that occurred during David's cleansing period and the challenging situations he had to go through during this process.

— Sherin Lee

As I myself began to get well, I then dealt with David's health issues and decided to have Dr. Lee treat him also. He was six years old at that time, and he began having multiple bloody noses. Not often at first, but then they increased to three times a day, with blood clots every time.

He continually experienced digestive problems and often complained of stomachaches after eating. From the age of two, he was frequently constipated and often struggled with having a daily bowel movement. His energy level was very low and his hunger was never satisfied; no matter what or how much he ate, he was still underweight.

So when Dr. Lee began his treatment, she began by giving him some of the same supplementation that I was taking, and it helped him tremendously. His bloody noses stopped within a month and his digestive problems lessened. He rarely complains of a stomachache now, and never ever calls for me while in the bathroom because he is struggling to have a bowel movement. I see his health improving every day. At times when he has gotten sick from a cold or the flu, he will even ask me to give him one of the herbal foods that he eats, saying it makes him feel better.

We did go through some difficult times before his health improved while taking his supplementation. He had always had fear issues because he saw what I went through when I was ill. Also, he had been sick with pneumonia — twice in one year — about two years prior to this. He had had an allergic reaction to an over-the-counter cough medicine: when given it, he had **ceased to breathe** on two different occasions. He never forgot that incident.

Dr. Lee mentioned that all these things had happened because David had many nutritional deficiencies and that his main problem was a sluggish bowel. We began increasing his fiber intake. She also said that he needed to cleanse and advised me to keep him home from school for two weeks. While cleansing, he would possibly get worse before his health improved — meaning his symptoms could become more intense. She knew the emotional and physical changes he was going to go through while cleansing. But I questioned the importance of keeping him home from school, however. Thinking he would be fine, I sent him to school anyway. Little did I know what was in store for him and me.

And it happened exactly as she had predicted. His fear and stomachaches became more intense, and he missed a lot of school because of this. Dr. Lee did mention that the reason he was so fearful was not just mental; that it had to do more with his not feeling well physically. She added that once David started feeling better physically, his fear would also start to go away.

The school had been made aware that he was engaged in a healing program, and that he was being seen by a Naturopathic Doctor. They were very helpful to David during this period. Because of his fear and anxiety, he was required to see the school's social worker. She also recommended that I seek therapy for him, which I did.

Dr. Lee had explained to me that much earlier in his life, David had accumulated much fear over the seriousness of my illness and that it would be necessary for him to be cleansed emotionally of his fear. With this cleansing would come the elimination of the fear. As I had experienced a similar emotional cleansing, I had an understanding of what my son was going through. Most challenging was balancing the understanding between the school's staff and the desires of my doctor regarding David's treatment.

Therapy was recommended by the school. I consoled myself with the fact that Dr. Lee knew *David did not need therapy*. But I allowed it, just to "keep the peace". I spoke briefly to the school staff about his condition, explaining very little — as explained to me, that this was a *natural* healing process. Of course he did become challenging at this time. But I thank God for many of the school's staff, because of their support and help that were needed during that difficult time.

* * * *

On one occasion when we were in session with the social worker, David became *very* angry — Dr. Lee had mentioned that he would have many strong emotions during his cleansing period. He didn't want me to leave his side, and was having a very difficult time attending and remaining at school every day It was an extremely stressful time. David had become very difficult to deal with, especially when he was left at school. So it was this time. This day the social worker and I were trying to convince him to stay, without success. And what happened next was unbelievable.

Now we are coming to the critical point where a rebirth begins to emerge. This is the actual process of retracing (going back in time to) various ills and emotional stressors. David's reluctance to be apart from his mother was certainly due to his earlier fear of losing her during the years of her illness.

— Sherin Lee

All of a sudden he screamed so loudly, crying out to me with his fists clenched and immense anger in his voice, **"You don't want me! You never wanted me — even when I was a baby!"**

The look in his eyes at that moment was as if he wasn't there. I couldn't believe what he was saying. I couldn't understand *how he knew....*

For when I was pregnant with David, I made a very difficult decision — *to abort him.* I was having a horrible pregnancy and felt that I would not be capable of handling it. The symptoms were so intense that they made it very difficult to deal with. I was extremely sensitive to light, sound, and odors; I also had extreme nausea all day, every day, and got no relief from prescribed medicine. (Eventually, with a different medicine for nausea given to cancer patients, these symptoms lessened a bit.) At this point I had a discussion with my husband, telling him about my decision to have an abortion. Right after this, however, I realized that I just couldn't do it. The thought of aborting my unborn child became much more difficult to deal with than my symptoms, and I decided to continue the pregnancy.

(It's no surprise to me why I ended up getting as ill as I did. Looking back, my health was already in trouble.)

So when David yelled out, I knew what he was referring to. But what I couldn't understand was *HOW COULD HE KNOW that I had almost ended his life before it had begun?* I was astounded over what had just happened! David was so upset that the social worker tried to grab him to calm him down, but he didn't want her to touch him and pulled away very angrily. So she kept her distance, with a very concerned look on her face. She then told me that there was definitely something serious that had to be "talked out" between David and I. I didn't mention anything to her because I wasn't sure she would believe me.

At the end of the school day, I almost couldn't wait to ask him about the incident. I asked him calmly why he had cried out like that. *"What are you talking about?"*, he asked with a confused look on his face. I explained to him in detail and he replied, *"I don't know what you're talking about. I never said that."* I then told him that he had, and he replied, saying very firmly, *"No, I didn't. I would never say that. Why would I say that?"* He had no recollection of saying those words and insisted he had never said that, even though he remembered other things he had said that morning at the social worker's office.

David's mind was now capable of cleansing past, burdensome thoughts without his *conscious* permission.
—Sherin Lee

I was in disbelief. So I told Dr. Lee about it and she was amazed that it had occurred but not surprised that it was possible. She had mentioned to me that a person may *retrace* (relive) past memories while cleansing, especially those buried in the subconscious mind. The fact that my son could go back and have remembrance while in the womb was not surprising. The real amazement about the incident was *the lack of **conscious** memory*. It was hard for me to believe and understand what she had explained to me that day, until it happened with David—I was astounded.

And I never asked David about it again. Dr. Lee advised me not to because, she said, there was no benefit to that memory since *it was only in his **subconscious** mind*. He just needed to "get it out" in order to heal, and that was all he needed to do. On one occasion, however, he overheard me tell his therapist about it; again his response was the same: that he had never said that. The therapist didn't know what to say about the whole thing and it was never mentioned again.

* * * *

Eventually things settled down at school for David. He ended his therapy, since as his health improved his fear subsided—just as Dr. Lee had said it would.

All in all it was a challenging situation, but I couldn't see doing it any other way. I felt this was a small sacrifice to make to unburden my child from unresolved issues. Without this experience of *cleansing*, he may have been in counseling for the next several years, and/or medicated. The only thing I would probably do differently would be to keep David home from school for the two weeks that Dr. Lee had advised. That way I don't think it would have gone so badly for him at school. But wouldn't we all do things differently if we could go back and make changes?

I don't need to know now why things happened the way they did. I *do* know that God always does things for a good reason. I felt Him saying that everything was going to be all right; this gave me peace of mind about my decision to seek out alternative medicine.

All I wanted was the best for David. I wanted to see him healthy and happy, without being on medication — and I believe he would've been on many of them, and gone through much more, if I had chosen a different route. Especially because of what *I* had gone through, with so many medications, I didn't want anything like that to happen to David. I felt I needed to try *this* route *first*, before putting him on any medications. I am still very thankful for medications, because there are times when they are really needed — for instance, when they kept me alive during those visits to the hospital ER when I was ill. *But there is a better way.*

I thank God for the support that Dr. Lee gave me while going through this crisis with David. I couldn't have done it without her help. She always made sure to remind me that no matter how difficult it got, it would all pay off in the end. She would also say to me that I should never allow anything or anyone to frighten me.

She said this because she knew there were times when I had doubts about my decision to try an alternative kind of medicine, since I had allowed the opinions of many others to confuse me when making decisions. So her encouraging words were a blessing to me.

And she was right again; it did pay off in the end: David's health is improving every day.

"Thank God we met Dr. Lee," David once said to me.

HEALTH BY ACCIDENT: GAYLE'S STORY

G ayle's story, told from a Registered Nurse's perspective, exemplifies the need for **natural medicine** in today's times — in that it is capable of bringing a person's health to a complete restoration.

I was looking for a way to find better health for a family member. We were carefully avoiding bad foods and being conscious of making healthy decisions; yet it didn't seem like we were finding good health. I realized we were avoiding the bad but weren't supporting our health. I researched Naturopaths to try and get some guidance about how to add health back into our lives.

This search led me to Dr. Sherin Lee. I was in her office with my family when she looked at me and offered to help me as well. She did not know I had reached a point where I was just plain worn out. I had had many years of maxed-out physical and mental demands — taking care of my kids, parents and their failing health, job, and marriage. Over a span of a few years I lost both parents and went through a divorce. I was in a place where I was drained, physically and emotionally. I was trying to get my health back and just couldn't figure out how to do it. My hair was thin, my eyelashes were thin, my skin was dry. I was tired all the time. I had frequent sinus and bladder infections. Most of my life I dealt with stomach pain—problems with certain foods which I tried to avoid. Being a Nurse, I felt I had a basis to process how to get healthy, but could not fix myself. I was avoiding certain foods, self-medicating with NSAIDs and at times prednisone for the severe abdominal pain.

Dr. Lee changed my life.

She looked at me and said, "Your liver has been under stress for a long time. Your GI system is out of balance." We talked about my diet, my habits, my stress and behaviors. Her compassion, intelligence, and observation of my needs amazed me. What she observed about me was on target. She patiently explained to me how everything connected with my health was happening in my colon. I was eating carbs and sugar to get quick energy, which was feeding the yeast and creating a leaking membrane. I knew these things but I never could get it right to fix the issue. She helped me see how overgrowth of yeast in my colon was causing so much trouble. I was so excited to start getting better when I left her office.

She painstakingly went through my diet and habits with me, so I could see where I was hurting myself. She supported me with kindness, information, honesty and observation, and helped me make adjustments so that I could understand what was going on in my body with the new changes. She tied all of me together. My spirit, my colon, my faith and hope.

I understand and am still amazed at how much I have learned about supporting and restoring cellular health. I feel so much clearer in my thinking. I can understand how critical cellular health and nutrient support of body systems are in order to have the base for strength and balance in my physical, emotional and spiritual health. I had thought I would have health by just relieving my symptoms. I am learning so much more about moving forward to not only sustain health, but to restore and rejuvenate all areas of my life. *It is great to feel empowered!* I now feel like I can change my health, and keep it there.

I have never felt better in my life than I do now. I have lost weight, not even trying. I have no more stomach pain, no bloating, a flat stomach (no cellulite anymore!!!). My hair is thick, my eyelashes are growing, my skin looks great, my eyes are white. I have no joint pain. I have crazy energy now. No more sinus or bladder infections. I will never stop the nutritional support that Dr. Lee planned for me. She is continuing to help me restore my health, with further concentration on cleansing my liver and balancing my body and spirit. This is how everyone should feel! For some reason, our society has made finding health so difficult. I have people notice now and ask me what am I doing. I send them to Dr. Lee. She coached me to this state. I am beyond grateful to her for giving me my health; it's the base for everything future.

— Gayle Lakie, RN, CCM, CCP

A Fortunate Coincidence:
Tallat's Story

A few words from Tallat Choudry, PhD, a colleague and a great friend. No matter what the condition, real change (on a cellular level, not merely suppressing symptoms) can be absolute.

I was very excited to have met Dr. Sherin Lee at a Naturopathic Conference almost twenty years ago. I have benefitted immensely from her natural healing advice and have recommended family and friends to her practice. I first came to Dr. Lee many years ago with stomach problems, among others. After seeking treatment with Dr. Lee, many conditions were deeply improved.

My spouse, Tauseef, also sought Dr. Lee for treatment. He has Parkinson's, which started five years ago and is in remission ever since he started taking herbal supplements through Sherin. The medications, herbal supplements, good nutritional foods, and being physically active have kept my spouse stable and among the top 5 percent who are in remission.

Dr. Lee is sensitive, intelligent, and extremely knowledgeable. She gives thorough guidance through personal one-on-one health talks during her consultations. You would be introduced to the best healthcare professional consultant and would receive your own in-depth nutritional and herbal guidance.

We are so proud and pleased to have Dr. Sherin Lee as our sincere holistic health advisor and friend. We wish her the best in her personal life and her health practice. Long live Sherin to be healthy, wealthy and wise!

— *Tallat Tauseef Choudry, PhD*

THE EDITOR'S OWN STORY

*D*avid Knezetich's story is important in showing how one can effect a change in one's health even after **decades**: All things are possible.

Other than allergies, I've been very fortunate not to have had any life-threatening, chronic, or debilitating health issues in my life (as of this writing, 63 years and counting). My allergies were active early on. I was taken to an allergist when I was five years old, because I had had a lot of head congestion and some sinus infections, with fevers, etc. My parents were told "he'll never outgrow his allergic condition".

The diet in our house was the typical "meat and potatoes" diet, with white bread and lots of milk, of course, in the America of the 1950's and 1960's—including some cooked vegetables, of which I would reluctantly eat small amounts. Surely my parents were following to a large degree the government's guidelines and recommendations of the time for nutrition—such as the "Food Pyramid". On the other hand, usually my father would add a salad of iceberg lettuce with olive oil, and salt and pepper—but I would avoid eating it as much as possible.

We would often have fruit canned in heavy syrup such as pears or peaches at our main meal. My parents were unable to interest me in eating fresh fruit. They often said it was a treat to them when growing up in America during the Depression years. To me it was nothing special or even of interest. Unfortunately, at the time I did not realize how profound were my father's words to me: "Remember, you are what you eat!".

In addition to the usual candy bars and other hard and soft candy, a favorite sweet of mine was "rock candy" — a chunk of pure, crystallized sugar! Other than spoiling one's appetite and causing tooth decay, at the time eating candy was not seen particularly as something one should limit — a fact which makes one wonder how many of my generation have developed diabetes at an early age....

Since my father had a sensitive stomach, the meat my mother cooked for dinner was broiled *REALLY* well-done — lamb chops that looked like cinders and dried-out steaks were a turn-off to me for years. This situation probably drew me to eat FAR too much of an "unholy trinity" of cheese, pizza, and hot dogs during my college and graduate school years and beyond. As I grew up, I was accompanied by the rise of "Fast Food". Basically, I would eat the least objectionable choice available to me. This eating pattern, including pretty much ignoring vegetables, continued through my completing school, entering the work force, and living on my own.

* * * *

I had known Dr. Lee since we were children. While in town to attend the funeral of one of her family members, I asked her to lunch after the service in order to "catch up" on events. At this time she told me what she did, about her practice as a Naturopath, after first explaining what a *"Naturopath"* was. I then thought about my own situation at this point in my life — my parents were both deceased, dying from heart attacks. My father also suffered from Alzheimer's disease and moderate Parkinson's disease, and my mother had developed mild diabetes later in life. At this time I was overweight, had a "spare tire" around my waist, and was often red-faced: I probably was not far from a stroke or a heart attack.

After listening to how she had raised herself from what she termed her own "hellish condition," I felt moved to work with her — it was almost instinctual. I had also remarked on the number of relatives who had passed away, some much before their time. My desire was to remain strong and independent in my later years. I had spent plenty of time visiting others in nursing homes, and I knew that scenario would not be for me.

I made an appointment and began to work with Dr. Lee. Her examination included checking my tongue and nails for indications of health issues, and also my eyes using *Iridology*, in which illness in the body is indicated or reflected in the iris of the eye.

Besides high blood pressure, an extremely high percentage of fat in my bloodstream was discovered. Of course, these were just further indicators that disaster was just around the corner if I didn't take action to improve my health.

I also had an underactive thyroid gland. My glandular system was out of balance, because I could feel adrenaline being released when I was startled, surprised, or just became very anxious about anything. From childhood I had always been a fearful person, with a passive personality; and I was still, even at the door of my senior years.

Finally, after Dr. Lee's asking about it, I acknowledged that my concentration was poor and my mental processes seemed to be "fuzzy", slow, and somewhat impaired.

We began to fix things, to set things right. Dr. Lee follows three principles of Chinese medicine: to **Nourish**, to **Balance**, to **Cleanse** the major systems of the body. It was obvious that I was not eating nutritiously, and she pointed out that my problem with mental concentration was clearly due to toxins and impurities in my body — including in my blood, which carried them through my entire system. As Dr. Lee has indicated in her own account, even one's vision can be affected by this situation! (She likens it to that of a car with a dirty oil filter.) A major cleansing — of body, mind, and emotions — was in order.

We got great results in a short time: My 38-inch waistline shrunk down to 34 inches, and I lost 20 pounds. Even better, my body-fat percentage decreased to a healthy number. As indicated by Iridology, my thyroid activity became balanced (and to this day my symptoms have not reoccurred). It was wonderful to notice how my mental processes and concentration became much clearer.

I also became much more confident and assertive.

The process itself was practically an emotional release. There seemed to be gradual improvement all along, but one day the majority of it all came out in a roar, like a great flood! *Feelings* and *emotions* that had been harbored for years, actually affecting me and interfering with my true being, needed to be released. I was finally able to express to people exactly what I had been holding back for years and years.

Perhaps the nicest thing of all was the situation with my allergies. I was getting allergy shots for over 40 years. After all this time, the same allergies remained, with little improvement.

Dr. Lee explained to me that my immunity had been weak from childhood and required strengthening. After we had worked for a while to do this, I made the decision to stop getting the shots. I simply felt — or *knew* — that *it was time*. I was friendly with the nurse at the clinic, and when I told her she surprised me by appearing to be so accepting about it. In any case, I often wondered what harm the substances from those shots, going into my body *for decades*, had done. Yet I was at peace, with the knowledge from Dr. Lee that whatever harm had been done could be corrected.

* * * *

Unfortunately, years later the next health hurdle I had to overcome was *shingles*. After previously strengthening my health under the guidance of Dr. Lee, I had gone "off track" by not taking care of myself and had allowed my immunity to weaken. In addition, my stress level had risen dramatically. So I had contributed to the flare-up. Dr. Lee explained to me that the virus had lain dormant in my bloodstream; my weakened immunity had allowed it to surface.

My shingles were painful enough that it was hard to have a restful sleep and it was unpleasant to move in bed. A few times, my back felt alternating sensations of warmth and cold; most often — besides feeling painful — it seemed like the skin on my back was being stretched tightly, sometimes in two directions as once.

Sherin to the rescue: She prescribed a regimen of herbal foods, vitamins, and minerals that beat my case of shingles in a few weeks. And the best sequel to *that* fact is that there has been no relapse to date. From telling my story to others, I have learned that cases of this type have taken months to years for improvement — and sometimes are without *any* improvement.

* * * *

Dr. Lee is fond of quoting the maxim: *"If your body is not REGENERATING, it is DEGENERATING!"* Through my association with her, I've learned that she possesses a wonderful, extensive, and innate understanding of the human body, and of how to allow it to regenerate and heal itself. And — as she herself would say — that *the body itself is its own best doctor,* when we smooth its path and enable it to do so.

Contact Information

Lee ND Natural Medicine
1114 North Larkin Avenue
Joliet, Illinois 60435 U.S.A.
Telephone: 815-744-0004

E-Mail:
LEE@LEENDNATURALMEDICINE.COM

Website:
LEENDNATURALMEDICINE.COM

David Knezetich
DRLEESASST1@YAHOO.COM

Veronica Rodriguez
LEESPA12V@YAHOO.COM

CPSIA information can be obtained
at www.ICGtesting.com
Printed in the USA
LVOW11s0734091017
551736LV00001B/61/P